Another **D**ysfunctional **H**ead **D**ay

Scott Bradshaw

Another Dysfunctional Head Day
written by Scott Bradshaw

Published by Tap Productions

ISBN: 978-0-9574828-0-7

Photographs: chrisbevanphotography.co.uk
Artwork: Kit Nelson

The Tapman's Intro

Hello. My name is Scott Bradshaw. At the age of 37 I discovered that I had a condition called ADHD, which at the time meant little or nothing to me. Clearly, however, it was thought to affect my behaviour in some way that was considered by those making the diagnosis to be unfavourable. Perhaps this might explain some of the problems I had encountered for all the years I could remember?

After initially struggling to come to terms with the possible implications of this realisation, I resolved to research the condition at every conceivable opportunity, and after more than 3 years of filling this gap in my knowledge on what I for one feel is still an under-researched field in lay-person's terms, I have decided it is right to address this glaring gap in our understanding, by combining the real - life experiences of others with those I have encountered throughout my life. Thereby, this book might just with any luck help you to learn how to deal with your own ADD ADHD, or that of someone close to you.

This book will aim to give you real information on the condition, and useful strategies to adopt when attempting to deal with the downsides of what can be a debilitating and frustrating condition, and further, it will attempt to go on to prove that many of the most successful people in the world historically may well have had one of the conditions that sits alongside ADD ADHD, though of course these have been recognised and linked only relatively recently.

When you have come to terms with and accepted that you have the condition, then and most likely only then, can you learn strategies which will help turn your life around, using ADHD to your advantage. I will show you first hand how I have accomplished this, and while I accept that some of my methods will not work for everyone, I feel confident that many people will find them very useful in dealing with their life on a day-to-day basis.

You will find I quite often use the phrase 'normals' throughout the text of this book. I must stress at this point that this is merely an example of my referring to those people unaffected by the condition for comparison's sake; never at any point am I attempting to separate these 'normals' from people with ADHD, or insinuate that one is in some way better than the other.

I know for certain that if I had known about this condition earlier in my life it might have been very different so I am hoping that in reading this book other people may uncover things they need to know at a much younger age than myself.

This book represents literally the good, the bad and the ugly about ADD ADHD, and is full of helpful tips on how to deal with real - life situations that people with the condition can quite often struggle with.

If you are wondering why I use the terms ADD and ADHD together a lot throughout the book, it is because they are very similar conditions, often confused by laymen, and adult ADHD is more often than not more like childhood ADD as the hyperactivity tends to disappear with age.

Some of the information in this book is based on currently - acknowledged fact; some of it is totally new based on first-hand account, and as such worthy of consideration in my view.

Too often, children with this condition have been, and continue to be, labelled by the genuinely unknowing or the lazily uncaring as "naughty" or "disruptive" children; this is totally and palpably untrue. Far too many have faced expulsion from school if they carry this label. Worse still are the lives blighted on a daily basis by degrading punishments, by days and weeks stood facing a wall and by detentions too numerous to count. Although some progress has been made, it is high time that serious resources were concentrated on countering this ongoing problem, which in my view is a damning indictment of the civilised and tolerant society some would have us believe we represent. I am sincerely hopeful that people will see this condition from a totally different angle after reading this book and that it will help people deal with ADHD where it exists and also with attitudes which they may encounter as a result.

I have on occasion used certain statistics throughout the course of the book but do not intend that these be treated in themselves as absolute truths, bearing in mind that many of the figures that are bandied around emanate from official government sources. Based on personal experience and research, I would say that the vast majority of these are a mile out. How very convenient for our elected representatives, with their vested interests!

Clearly, there will be points in this book that some people do not agree with, from their perspective or experiences. I accept that all such perceptions are personal and subjective (and are equally valid) but I would stress I am not a doctor and this isn't meant to read as a medical textbook, and further, as I have no connection with either the educational or medical establishment (other than as an end-user!) I am able to place my own experiences and feelings in normal words rather than the professional jargon of doctors and educators. In this way I hope to tell you more about how things actually are in the here and now, not just sepia-tinted graphs of how it has been in the past!

The fact is, the average doctor simply wouldn't be minded or allowed to say some of things that I have said in this book, based on my many meetings over the years with professionals in this field. I have formed the impression that they are mostly a bit defensive, worried even, about potential changes to the system as it exists and has existed for some time. How can we improve this system if no one has the capacity to suggest - and even try - new methods?

I must apologise if, in the course of the book, some ideas or notions appear as repetition. While as a relative novice author I humbly admit in advance these may represent genuine oversight on my part, my plea in mitigation is that I have attempted to make allowance for the fact that readers with ADD ADHD may in fact benefit from such repetition. My contention is that, where a point needs making, it is better it be made twice than that it go astray, another unnoticed victim of the condition.

Section 1

1. What is ADHD? ....linked conditions

ATTENTION DEFICIT HYPERACTIVITY DISORDER

What is ADHD? ...well perhaps I'd do well to leave definitions to the medical profession – after all, they are the ones that know...or are they?

The reason that I originally decided to write this book was that, despite having read seemingly every book available on this condition, I am still to find one yet that I can totally relate to, or to rely upon for practical help. Sometimes the best way to be given information on a condition like this is "straight from the horses mouth" so to speak, that is, someone like me, one who has learnt how to deal with some of the compromising situations that all with the condition are familiar with.

I make no secret of saying that I don't think the people "in the know" have got this condition right at all, as it is such an individualised condition and one which is "understood" outside of its rightful context in so many instances.

SOME OF THE COMMON SYMPTOMS TO LOOK OUT FOR

Struggle to remember basic daily routine things.

Don't seem to listen when being spoken to.

Don't seem to follow instructions.

Quite often leave tasks unfinished.

Cannot pay attention for long periods of time.

Very easily distracted by others or by oneself.

Quite often find oneself in trouble, especially at school.

Sometimes display a very short temper.

Will only pay attention to things that are of interest.

Talk excessively, sometimes without seemingly making any sense.

Displays big problems with participating in conversation without butting in.

Quite often can't sit still and very fidgety.

Quite often will simply not do as told or instructed.

Has a big problem with authority and taking instructions.

Quite often likes to be the centre of attention.

Can cry readily, and prone to throwing tantrums.

Put simply, ADHD is a minor brain dysfunction caused by an inbalance of the neurotransmitter chemicals noradrenaline and dopamine. This leads to hyperactivity and agitation, often in inappropriate social contexts, which can also lead to anxiety and depression, even in children.

Those with ADHD often display very bad impulse control and because of this can quite often inadvertently talk themselves into trouble and also can be very accident prone.

There are a number of conditions which sit along side ADD and ADHD and they are as follows:

O.C.D. - obsessive compulsive disorder.

O.D.D. - obsessive defiant disorder.

A.D.D. - attention deficit disorder.

Aspergers syndrome.

Depression and Anxiety

Other conditions that are very closely related are as follows:

Bi-polar disorder

Conduct disorder.

Learning disorders.

Tourette's syndrome.

Dyslexia

One statistic which is clearly unsatisfactory (if true) suggests that 48% of children diagnosed with one of the following disorders (A.D.D., A.D.H.D., Bi Polar, Dyslexia and O.C.D.) will show signs of the other four by the time they are fifteen years of age.

This is a lifelong and possibly life-threatening condition and although with time and experience it can be managed, it will never go away. This is why I believe that you need to learn how to deal with your condition through personal experience, in your own way, and preferably without the use of mind-altering drugs, readily and liberally prescribed by a medical profession which has a cosy relationship with the pharmaceutical industry. Obviously I am neither a doctor nor a politician, and I won't be attempting here to delve into medical matters in great detail, as this book is merely designed to help you understand, and learn how to deal, with your condition and more importantly, how to learn how to use it to your advantage.

Far too many children are excluded each year from school because of ADD or ADHD although, as I myself have learnt at first hand, as we get older it is something that can really become a massive advantage to have. In fact, it isn't all doom and gloom folks - but if you don't learn how to control your condition, you will be in for a life of trouble, and you will also find that any progress will be very slow. In the worst cases you may fall foul of the police, and in really extreme instances you could end up dead. It really is just that serious! You will find that you leave a trail of destruction after you and you will also find that you will spend much of your life arguing with anyone and everyone if you don't learn how to control yourself - the sooner, the better!

Some good news is that only 50% of children carry the symptoms into adulthood but this is not because the condition goes away. As I said before, we are dealing with a lifelong condition that will always need attention and a lot of self-discipline if you want to make a success of your life.

For loved ones - don't be too upset if you find out that your child has been diagnosed with ADHD. You may just find that it can actually be an amazing gift and indeed, many of the most successful people in life have this, or one of its ancillary conditions.

To make this book a little easier to read (and knowing first-hand how bad concentration levels can be) I decided at the outset to write with little or no set order, rather writing sections in a more free-flowing manner, hoping to give the more frank and honest depiction of one who lives each day with the condition a constant companion, like some invisible or unknown family member. With luck, this will be something that anyone with this condition will be totally able to relate to, and there are also some examples to break down the reading!

Although I aim to include a lot of useful information that will hopefully help you or your children learn how to succeed with this condition, please note that you may find it of interest to research further some of the topics raised in the book yourself, as there are many different opinions on certain aspects of this condition, and this book merely reflects my own opinions and experiences. However, I feel sure you will be able to take at least something positive away after reading it!

2. Family Problems

Where do I start on this one? This is one of the biggest problems in the life of people with ADD ADHD and yet it doesn't seem to be documented to any great degree in any of the books around at the moment. The toll that lots of little arguments and bickering can take on a family relationship generally goes unnoticed on an everyday basis but over a period of time can be thoroughly devastating to all aspects of family life. As an only child the only people that were really affected in my family were my mum, dad and myself. Now, at the age of 40, I can see the damage that this condition has done to my close family, but in all honesty I have only really noticed this in recent years.

This damage starts to become apparent the first time that a child or teenager gets into serious trouble. I recall vividly the first time I landed myself in trouble with the police and my mother's reaction was to say, "What have I done to deserve you as a son?" I'm afraid I still get similar reactions even now, but these days thankfully it's more playful joshing than anything designed to wound.

The real problem that ADD ADHD creates within a family environment is that relationships become very hostile and quickly become the norm, a default setting if you will. In extreme cases parents can literally end up hating their children and vice versa. Obviously this can cause big problems throughout the family, especially where it's a big family. As I said earlier, I am an only child so our family feuds haven't been between many people but if you are from a larger family then the problems can be much bigger and more spread out. Even where, say, there are pairs of brothers and sisters in the family the chances of only one child having the condition are very slim. Remember that ADD ADHD is hereditary so there isn't much chance that anyone will be left out when the family genes are handed out at birth. However, the possibilities for groups to form within the family which isolate individual family members are greatly increased.

I have spent my last four summers living with people with this condition in an attempt to try to understand how it would be to live in a normal family household where ADD ADHD runs strongly throughout the family. One of the main things I noticed is that three - and four-way arguments in these situations don't often happen, and most fallouts are usually between two people; not very often did I witness others getting drawn in. In fact, it was quite the opposite, with people usually not wanting to get involved in what is after all familiar behaviour!

When it comes to parents, it's a similar thing, although nine times out of ten the parents will stick together as a pair to try and instil discipline in the child.

HOW THEY WORK

You might also find that you have some family problems the day you tell your parents that you think you have a condition. Looking back, I went about it the wrong way when I told my parents I couldn't understand why they weren't full of sympathy, whilst in fact I felt they were quite cool to me. Looking back, I think this is what set me on this mission to raise awareness about the condition, because it is vital that we have as much support around us as possible when we decide to attempt once and for all to master the condition.

What I for one didn't take into account was the fact that maybe my parents just didn't want to believe that their son was actually in some way "imperfect", and more to the point had a neurological, a "mental" condition. Even now, we seldom if ever talk about ADHD, as they are still a little bit in denial that it exists and exactly how it could affect someone apparently in so many different ways. It's sadly true that still, any conversation I have with my parents around ADHD always ends in me having to leave the house before I say something that I know I will regret. In fact, this has been one of the most frustrating things I've ever had to deal with to be honest, and has caused me a lot of problems, particularly having to deal with everything on my own, without sibling help. I genuinely hope that after reading this book their opinion on or attitudes to the condition might change. I don't know if they will ever believe my contention that it's more a gift than a hindrance - well maybe they will if our film, conceived as complementary to the book, is a big hit?

I really regret the two or three years that I haven't really got on with my parents. It's a great sadness to me, and I would turn the clock back instantly to change it. My advice here would be, don't push this condition on your parents in the way I did! They are from a different generation and will always see things from a totally different angle to you. Also, remember there's a good chance that one or both of them might well have the condition themselves and we have seen what happens when family members with ADD ADHD argue, it usually ends in tears!

3. Dealing with ADHD

As has been said, it is absolutely crucial that you find a way to devise a workable strategy to make good use of this supposed mental condition. Personally, I hate people referring to it like that but technically this is correct: on paper (and on medical files!) people with ADD ADHD are not 'normal' compared with the bulk of the population. The secret to dealing with this undeniable fact is to begin by telling yourself that you are merely a little different to the average; this doesn't in any way imply that you will go on to lead a life different in any respect to that of an average person. Whilst there is no cure as such to the condition, fifty per cent of the task of devising a coping strategy lies in recognising that it exists and has affected your life and those around you. Only after accepting this fact can you go on to deal with it and eventually, in turn, use it to your advantage.

Another massively important element in dealing with your ADD ADHD is that your family and those close friends around you have to accept the fact that you are, and will continue to be, a little different to 'normals'. This doesn't mean that they need to treat you any differently but it would be very wise if they were to read up on the condition, as at least this way they might be able to understand the underlying causes to our reacting to situations in the ways that we often do.

Another area that needs addressing in a wider context is the continuing and ill-informed stigma that the condition attracts. This invariably seeps into the school classroom, often with disastrous results. We tire of hearing about kids getting labelled and often excluded from school because of ADD ADHD, diagnosed or not, and these children are being alienated and socially isolated for no reason whatsoever. How can kids even start to deal with this condition if they are being made to feel - and look - like they are a different breed of human? Personally I think it's pretty nigh impossible for kids to be taught properly how to deal with this until they reach the ages of between eight and ten; of course, it won't do any harm to show them early on how to deal with certain situations but there is little to be gained in educating them properly about ADD ADHD until they are that little bit older and actually understand life - and their part in the scheme of things - a bit more.

While at first I was pretty angry that even by middle age I still hadn't heard of the condition, after reading up on it and working out a strategy to adopt that I felt could be best for me, I decided to film myself in all sorts of different moods and situations and then post them on the website You Tube for other people to see, and hopefully to garner some feedback. I have to say, the response I received was amazing!

The videos have now had over 120,000 hits and have been used by certain schools that specialise in ADD ADHD to show the pupils. The reason for this success I think is that it is often easier, especially in view of a short attention span, to sit and watch something of interest rather than reading from "textbooks", which will most likely be seen as just plain boring. The results have been a big surprise, and a vindication of the strategy I adopted. To see documented footage of how I faced up to all aspects of this condition has helped a lot of people in their quest for similar goals and although personally embarrassing at times, I have decided to leave them there for all to view. The way I see it is, if they help just one person come to terms with it all then they are worth letting people see, and if some people don't care to watch them for whatever reason, then I'd say, don't!

One last bit of advice for now on dealing with ADD ADHD is to read up on all you can, watch the You Tube videos and try and get the people around you to do the same and before you know it you might just find that things that were a problem are now less so, or better still have disappeared completely!

Remember that fact: 50% of the "cure" lies in knowing that you have the condition in the first instance!

If you think a friend or family member might have ADD ADHD, sit them down on their own and tell them a bit about it, maybe buy them a book to read up on it, try to encourage them by telling them about the positive side to the condition instead of them having to listen to some of the nonsense that is said about it!

Personally, now I have learnt how to deal with it, I wouldn't want to be any other way! Some may say we're a bit crackers, a bit nuts, but look at the history books and you will see a pattern! So many of the major players, the very successful artists, scientists and elite sportsmen and women have been called at some time a little bit nuts!

It seems to become a top person in the normal world you have to be a bit different; they often talk of *ambition*. Maybe having ADD ADHD just gives you the edge in terms of ambition, after all!

4. Food and Drink

This was originally intended as a very detailed section of the book, giving useful advice on what would be good for your kids to eat or to avoid. However, as I researched the topic further, I soon learned that there is little if any actual proof that different foods and drinks affect children and adults with ADD ADHD to any significant degree.

How many times have we heard people saying what you can and can't give people with ADHD, how kids are likely to run up the walls after drinking fizzy pop and how chocolate turns them into monsters? Now while I must stress that I'm not saying that it is a good idea to give kids with ADHD these things in their diet, what I would say is that they are no more likely to be affected than anyone else drinking or eating the same things. We all know that it's wise to give children fizzy pop only sparingly, and I'm sure we have all witnessed hyperactive kids bouncing off the walls on drinks full of artificial colours and additives. E numbers are largely best avoided where possible. This however is just common sense which should apply to all children. There is definitely not enough evidence around to suggest you should forbid your kids the odd treat, but it should be monitored very carefully. You as parents are best placed to see what these foods and drinks are doing to your child's behaviour and only you can decide whether these should be allowed or not!

You can use the above treats-or, indeed, healthy alternatives - as rewards for doing homework or for any good behaviour. If you want to learn more about what food to give your kids I would suggest you either consult a specialist dietician-your GP should be able to assist with this - or you might try researching it a bit yourself. There are plenty of books available that can give you valuable information on the subject, and the internet is also a great place to find out good information, but be sure choose your pointers carefully, as this is most certainly an area where many people hold conflicting opinions.

I'm afraid that I remain uncertain about the different views on this matter and therefore I will refrain from going into anymore detail on it at this point. It is in my view a worthy subject for further research by those suitably qualified, and one I would like to return to in the future, but for now it up to you as parents to decide what best suits your particular situation.

One small bit of advice is to avoid white sugar whether it be in it's pure form or in drinks, cakes, sweets, etc. White sugar calcifies the pineal gland and over time could well increase the symtoms of ADHD. Read the sugar content of labels on food and it will certainly surprise you.

5. ADHD in Kids

There are many books which cover this subject in great detail and as it is again quite a complex area I intend to summarise what I see as the really crucial factors which will help you to notice if your child has ADHD and more importantly, what to do if you have your suspicions about a child or even an adult in your family.

It is possible to spot ADHD from a very young age but clearly you have to know what to look for. At toddler age you will find very irregular sleeping patterns, and you will find that your child will move around the bed a lot. You will find that up until what's commonly referred to as "the terrible twos" your child will drink up to double the amount of water during the night than is normal in a child of that age, and they will quite often wake up to have drinks. Always make sure you leave a bottle by them as during the night you will be surprised by how many times they do wake up in order to take a drink.

Another very obvious thing to look out for are tantrums and screaming fits, which can of course be quite scary at times but a keeping a cool head in these circumstances is paramount and you will find that your calm will help reassure the child.

Similarly, headbutting objects and sometimes walls and even parents themselves is another strong indication that your child might have the condition. My youngest son didn't sleep a full night until he was 20 months old and I was the same, not sleeping at all well till 18 months and even then, only by dint of a trip out in the car to help! If you are having these problems then motion is one answer. Whether it be a car or a rocking system ADHD babies and toddlers sleep much better when moving! If your child does throw a tantrum, try to occupy their mind instantly with something else totally different which may help divert their attention: "look at this!", as you grab a favourite toy may sometimes help to calm them slightly. Although this won't work all the time, I have found it to have a decent success rate.

Intelligent toddlers - that's what I call kids with ADD ADHD: buzzing around like little bees and spending nearly all of their time smiling or screaming, one or the other. However, they also in general have the ability to learn things very quickly and quite often will insist on doing things for themselves, unless or until they get frustrated and throw a tantrum. Allowances must be made for such frustrations, and independence encouraged. These talents are manifested from a very young age, and this can be one of the most entertaining periods for parents, though by the same token it can also be very difficult. Sensitivity is required!

My boys are both very similar to me, and it would appear that I must have strong genes. They look like I did at their respective ages and they act very similar, to boot. Does this mean they will have ADHD as bad, or even worse than me? This is another one for the scientists to look into but in the research I have seen I can discern a definite pattern of the condition in families and personally I think this trend may be increasing. 'Does this possibly get stronger with each generation?' is a question I find I ask myself regularly, though it's not a fact as yet, by the way!

Children with this condition will be inclined to play on their own a lot and really struggle with the ability to share things, especially at nursery or pre-school.

Obviously it makes very good sense to watch what your children eat and drink but it is unproven that additives affect ADHD children any different to any others! As your child grows up, and right to the point of the teenage years, you may possibly begin to see the hyperactivity start to go away but this is when the rebelling phase can take over. It's not that the hyper side is going anywhere new by the way, it is simply that I have found that this seems to be the first stages of the child starting to control the ADHD on his/her own.

You might not have got to this stage naturally as your doctor could previous to this have convinced you to give your child mind-altering drugs to control the symptoms, something which I personally would warn against in the strongest possible terms! Children as young as three are being treated with these drugs, and personally the thought of creative kids getting turned into something akin to zombies just horrifies me!

Start to educate your child about the condition from the age of eight upwards, especially if you have grown up with it yourself. Later in the book I will talk about ways of doing this but this condition is hard to diagnose and as stated fifty per cent of the 'cure' lies in acknowledging that you have it and later, learning how to deal with it!

Let's try and change the status quo, and stop these kids from being labelled at an unfeasibly early age as naughty kids. It will undoubtedly take a lot of time to repair the damage that this label has caused to people with this condition. For a start we could begin by talking about ADHD children as they should be - that is, among the most talented kids on the planet, who just need good direction and mentoring in something that interests them. Don't worry too much about your offspring's childhood being a bit different from others', as although it can be a massive problem through the school years, your child can grow into an adult that is very special and very talented indeed!

Learning about the condition as an adult is a lot harder, believe me on that one! So take my advice and be honest with your kids, it will only help them in the future!

6. ADHD in Schools

There always has been and there always will be an element in every classroom which may rightly be termed "naughty kids", but this ignores the fact that much of what happens in schools involving this condition is totally arbitrary and manifestly unjust, and really needs sorting out!

I am in close contact with a friend who is the head at a school for children with ADD ADHD and he hit the nail right on the head when I last spoke to him about this. What he said has been a truth throughout the ages: "there are naughty kids - and then there are *really* naughty kids!"

One type tends to talk a lot and enjoy the odd joke, and the other type hit teachers and burn schools down or similar. The fact that there is a world of difference between the two groups doesn't seem to be recognised, and therein lies the problem. The result is that *really* naughty kids are instantly diagnosed with the condition, which in my opinion is lazy and unjust.

The fact that you have ADHD doesn't mean for a moment that you are likely to attack a teacher or commit any other misdemeanour for that matter. Quite simply, there must be much better diagnosis!

The children that are the really big problem, the ones who commit the really serious offences at school, may have other issues quite separate to ADD ADHD, which need to be addressed quite differently. As things stand, these problematic children are often getting specialist help, but of a kind which they don't need and which won't benefit them at all, while these valuable resources might be better aimed at the children who might really need this help. If we are to be totally honest, it is well acknowledged that some of the more difficult cases need an awful lot more than either a special school or a dose of ritalin thrown down their necks can realistically offer. Whilst these are real and massive problems, why should the two separate groups be so lazily lumped together, to no-one's benefit? This is plainly wrong, and needs addressing as quickly as possible. Too many schools use our condition as an excuse to exclude children that cause minor problems when all they need is educating in a slightly different way! Most of the time these kids are the most creative and intelligent in the class, but as it is, the current schooling system just bores them to death. I have gone into more detail on this in the section about school education.

It is agreed that some children can cause a degree of disruption in the classroom but do they really deserve to made out to be something that they plainly are not, carrying a label they certainly don't deserve to be given which may stay with them for the rest of their lives, namely, that of a child who has a mental condition? I think not!

Educators, and the medical profession, have long been lazy when it comes to diagnosis of this condition, and they often give up way too easily! It's as if they have been handed an excuse to get rid of any children that make their life that bit harder! Sending them to the naughty corner is an easier option than trying to give them something constructive to do instead of expecting these kids to sit there and listen to the boring stuff that just doesn't interest them in the slightest!

"Known by everyone, liked by none" is one of the quotes that I recently read in another book on this condition and if I'm honest I can see where they get this idea from, even though it doesn't sit easily with me one bit!

I remember as a child always being very playful, always joking around and generally having a good time - until it came to the classroom, when it became more a question of pot luck and down to what mood I was in than what was being taught!

That said, I remember being very popular at times, especially when joking around but I also remember feeling very left out at times as quite often some people (even my friends) just didn't want to be around me. I could never figure out why back then but it is much clearer after researching the condition and seeing just how overpowering a child with ADHD can be, not only to other pupils but also to teachers.

You do find that children with this condition will to a degree be attracted to each other and this quite often spells trouble at school as they will constantly get each other into bother. On the other end of the scale, you will find that some kids with ADHD are very quiet and shy at school, and only find their real place in the world when they leave and follow their own path in life. School is a very lonely place for these kids and they are quite often bullied and ridiculed up to a point at which they rebel. A word of warning here: these children will have a breaking point at which, when pushed over the line, the reaction that you get from them may well prove alarming! What you may have taken for a quiet and unassuming child may easily turn into a minor monster and swiftly punish all who have bothered them in the past. My own school years made me very resentful to certain pupils and I'm rather embarrassed to admit that I spent a lot of time (even into adulthood) making sure I got each and everyone of them back! People with ADHD do have a problem with revenge and this is something that can land even the quietest in deep water.

ADD ADHD just wasn't recognised when I was at school, and as time goes on and more and more people are learning about it, let's hope that the school years can be much kinder to children with this condition than they have been in the past.

What happens at school can make or break you in the real world and it is vitally important that kids are not mentally scarred from their childhood experiences!

7. Have you done your homework?

As a parent I now know how hard it is to get children to do homework. Especially so as I was myself something of a genius at avoiding it. I was a total master at it, making up excuse after excuse and telling white lie after white lie to sneak out of doing what I felt at the time to be one of the worst things in the world.

If your kids have ADD ADHD I would say you're in for a very rocky ride when it comes to doing homework and I'm afraid to say it may well become a major bone of contention between you and them.

They seem to give homework from a much younger age than was the case when I was at school and, in the real world, that just means more and more arguing and fussing when it comes to this dreaded subject.

Television and computer games are one of the big obstacles when it comes to homework and a good piece of advice for you is to insist that there are no TV or games until homework is completed. It may be you feel it's okay to let them have fifteen minutes of TV after school - but then get straight into the homework, preferably in a quiet environment, with no distractions.

A good incentive for getting homework completed on time is to offer rewards - this is especially good for younger children. There is a lot of information on "reward charts" on the internet, and I suggest you take a look at it, as it could help in your quest for a peaceful household!

One thing is for certain, you as parents must be involved in your child's homework and you will almost always have to supervise it. If you leave your children to tackle homework on their own, there's a good chance that they will either not do it at all or do it very badly, and this will be apparent from the teacher when you go to your next parent's evening!

It is best to have a specific plan for homework which you stick to each and every day and this includes a place in the house that you can use each night to complete the task. If there's a day that your child is really struggling then the best option is to leave it for the day as it will save a major argument, and when the child is in this frame of mind you may as well just bang your head against the proverbial brick wall if you expect them to complete it!

Have a definite routine that allows your child a break if needed, and under no circumstances allow treats until the session is finished to everyone's satisfaction. These treats will act as a massive incentive to get the job done and the more this routine is followed, the easier it will become, even if they have had a bad day at school!

There is a break from the norm in the summer months that can definitely help: why not try taking your child to a park and sit down there to do their homework, maybe even bring a snack, and make a small event out of it. After all if there are swings and playthings in sight, this might just offer some much-needed encouragement to complete the task in a timely fashion!

Wherever possible you should encourage children with ADHD to do their homework on a computer, as they don't generally care for writing and are prone to mistakes whilst doing so. Anything that can make the homework more interesting or rewarding for the child can only be a good thing and you will find good results if you switch to this system!

Remember that teachers will punish your child if homework is incomplete so you have every right to discourage your child from cutting corners at home! The thought of detention really upsets kids with ADHD but being locked in their bedrooms with no video games is equally as hard to deal with. It is definitely better to reward children than to punish them though and this is something you should work towards.

You will find that your child will feel a massive sense of achievement once homework is complete, and it will put them in a much better mood for the rest of the day. However, get this wrong and you will find that your child will be awkward and moody thenceforth....prevention is certainly better than cure!!

Try to make homework fun and rewarding and it will make your life much easier and you won't have anywhere near as many arguments with your children!

8. School Education

Where to begin, really? The journey through school is the hardest single part in life for people with ADD ADHD. Quite often ridiculed by both pupils and teachers, they rarely fit in easily to this most regimented of environments.

The current education system has been around for over one hundred years and hasn't really changed that much at all - all the standard ways of educating kids have been the same forever! There have been exceptions, chiefly in the religious and private sphere, but these certainly haven't been available to all.

In the standard system, pupils are put into groups depending on how clever they are. When I was at school the people who were supposed to be less gifted were naturally expected to go on to be bricklayers or work in other building trades, but have you seen how much a bricklayer or a plumber can earn today? This is a perfect example of how it doesn't really matter how well you do at school in terms of how far you will go in life, although conversely, school can damage some kids forever and many literally never recover from it. I was always in trouble at school and only just scraped through several of the exams or tests by the skin of my teeth. I don't subscribe to the conventional wisdom that this was a direct result of a lack of ability; I simply just couldn't be bothered and if I'm totally honest I have to admit the whole education system just bored the hell out of me.

How many of the Dragons from TV series Dragons Den excelled in school? I would bet most of them left at fifteen and went into business. Richard Branson started selling things from phone boxes at the age of 15 and rarely attended his classes-I think it's fair to say that he has done ok now!

Like it or not, the fact is, the current education system goes totally against all the things that a child with ADD ADHD wants and wishes for. I can remember most of the kids that were brilliant at sport were not very good at the academic side and if I look at some of the people from my years at school who have gone on to achieve great things since leaving, most of them were not that bright at school and most spent a lot of time in the naughty corner - with me (haha!).

If you have a child that loves building things or creating things then it is like handing down a death sentence to expect them to sit through English lessons or language classes.

Schools in Spain, for example, don't seem to operate the same system as we do here in the UK and from what I've seen it seems to work well - maybe the time has come for a revamp of the United Kingdom's education system?

Despite recent moves toward "Social Inclusion" that sound great in principle but which in reality turn out to be somewhat less successful than advertised, maybe it's time that the education system looked at children with ADD ADHD or any of the ancillary conditions differently!

I think it's great that the supposed failures from school are often going on to do great things after school, and once they are released from the dreaded ball and chain of education, they can go on to flourish and do really well in life. It seems quite obvious to me that creative kids don't like being locked up in classrooms learning about things that are of absolutely no use to them whatsoever. This system just encourages them to misbehave as they are more often than not bored to tears and can't handle the sitting still for long periods of time and constantly being told what to do.

My idea would be to let the parents have much greater input and for schools to offer a lot more choice within the curriculum. In the USA such conditions allow special education classes for those in need of them, and although to many this may sound a bit extreme, it has to be better than forcing otherwise independent kids to learn about things they have no interest in.

There are schools in the UK that deal with particularly wayward children but I really think they should be only used in the really extreme cases of prolonged and exceptional misbehaviour. The problem is that others are and always have been classified in a similar way and, really, these days we should face up to the fact that the naughty kids are not always the ones that have ADHD. It's just a convenient fit to label them in that way! Habitually naughty children are making the good kids with this condition get the same label as they have and it's quite clearly incorrect!

Mainstream schools could still all have a class that accommodates those with ADD ADHD, not necessarily even a separate curriculum, just some classes slanted slightly differently that will give these kids something to learn about which might prove more of interest to them.

We are not thick! That's the message, simple as that, the truth is we can't, and shouldn't be expected to, concentrate on something that doesn't interest us and this is a good enough reason I believe to change things even slightly as it will help such children - many gifted, remember - to stay at school and more importantly they will learn things that will benefit them whilst recognising the way that they are!

Perhaps there might be one lesson a week where a class sit together and watch videos on ADHD and similar conditions, where they are encouraged to discuss and share their own experiences, while helping educate them in how to control their condition and thereby we may begin to alleviate many of the problems they have faced during a typical school day. We could perhaps have more craftwork and art classes for these types and maybe even set up film - making classes and teach how to operate camera and lighting equipment from a much younger age. In the digital era, such machinery has never been so readily available and so cheap, after all. The old excuses don't wash these days.

These are all things that kids with a condition will really enjoy and as long as they are enjoying something, they will show a lot of interest and more importantly, learn from practical skills, transferrable in the world after school!

It saddens and angers me to hear of schools which are still excluding and suspending kids that are labelled with these conditions when, as we can see, it can easily be so much better.

I was told recently when researching this section that one parent had been told that if their child didn't take the medication that was on offer to them they would not be allowed to attend school. This seems to me to be wrong on so many levels that for the life of me I can't understand how anyone would seek to defend it. I am no fan of giving children mind altering drugs anyway, and never have been, having seen the damage they can cause. The fact that a child might be expelled from school if they don't accede to this decree seems more than a bit strange to me and reeks of fear! It is something I certainly intend to look into.

No educator should be allowed to hand out rules like this seemingly on a whim, and although I well understand how problematic some of these children can be, there simply has to be a better way of dealing with situations like this!

No-one should be forced to take or dispense medication against their will, it is simply not right. Similarly, the "three strikes and you're out" system that some schools currently operate simply isn't fair to those with ADD ADHD. Let's be perfectly clear: we are talking about someone's life here, not some game of chance!

I don't in all honesty know what the perfect solution to any of the above is, or even if it exists, but what is clear is that the current system isn't offering a fair chance to the most vulnerable and disadvantaged in society, and a new way forward needs to be found - the sooner, the better!

9. I'm Bored!

I always intended that this book would accurately reflect many of the everyday situations that I encounter. Strange but quite fitting then, that sat this morning with my wife we should simultaneously exclaim the same words: "I'm bored!". Obviously, I know nothing of your boredom threshold, but mine for one seems to have been set precariously low at birth! Boredom can cause a person with ADHD big problems and this is a topic which feeds into so many aspects of behaviour covered throughout this book.

Bored as I was earlier, I see this as the perfect time to address this section of the book!

Whether it be a lack of willpower, a bad idea or the desire for a full-on blowout, boredom can encourage all sorts of negative situations - situations in which in which you won't be seen at your best!

How often do you hear your own kids say the dreaded words, "I'm bored!" and you instantly have to turn your attention to occupying their minds? Well, you can literally multiply the burden by five if you are dealing with a bored child with ADHD.

Many parents may not agree with my advice for the bored child, but hopefully they may agree on a lot of other points I make, so in an effort at honesty, I'll admit I have concluded that you can't beat a good old computer game to occupy the minds of these children! Obviously a game of football or a nice walk is preferable in most instances, but if the weather is poor or nothing else is working, your console game of choice will often do the trick. Children and adults with ADD or ADHD seem to be able to concentrate on gaming a lot more than a child without the condition. This is because their style of learning leans toward the kinaesthetic, meaning they respond better to "hands-on" learning, rather than to auditory or visual systems (as elaborated upon by David Kolb, and Honey and Mumford, amongst others). It is also one area that gives lie to the theory that people with ADHD cannot sustain concentration for long periods of time. If they are doing something that interests them, or which they connect with, then they will happily do that for hours on end. This is what I call "The Hyperfocus Button", and you will hear a lot more of this magic wand that people with ADHD are gifted with throughout this book.

What is the response of the average adult to boredom? How often does he or she fall back on the socially-conditioned reaction? Here, addiction may come into play, quite often a trip to the shop for some alcohol may ensue, or in other cases a phone call to a local dealer for something else to take the boredom away: basically anything that is different to what you are currently doing will suffice.

When there are a gang of kids hanging around the street and one decides they are bored, this can lead to big trouble for everyone, as often they won't have money to go bowling or some similar inoffensive entertainment and very often dares and suchlike 'naughty games' will ensue, being the only thing that satisfies the minds in these situations. Obviously this is never good and will often lead to trouble, sometimes with the police involved, and as life goes on the stakes can be raised a lot higher! I have known a guy climb up six levels of scaffold because he and his friends were bored. And another who not once but THREE times attempted to scale a local landmark chimney. The Fire Brigade officers were on first-name terms! Only when sober or on his own will this type of guy realise just how stupid he has been and then he will instantly regret his actions.

Bored in the classroom, a classic ADD ADHD problem! A lack of concentration, disturbing the rest of the class, quite often in trouble and always the joker. All things that in my opinion prove the current education system doesn't cater for children with this condition! However, as we have seen, when their minds are occupied with something that they enjoy or find fascinating they will sustain concentration longer than a 'normal' child. I feel that these children need to be given tasks which will constantly absorb them at school and everything needs to be made interesting for them to keep them keen! This is why creative tasks are a massive favourite for kids with ADD ADHD. Because conventional lessons don't address their needs shouldn't mean they are thrown by the wayside, discarded as in some way inferior.

It's a fact that it's very hard to get bored when totally occupied, and although this is a big challenge for parents of kids with this condition it is equally as hard for adults in the same situation. In the old days I would have looked for something to get up to, knowing that would alleviate the boredom, but these days I find I'd rather do something creative, like maybe make a film, or write a book or something (just a little joke, if you're wondering) but in all honesty as you get older you do find more ways to occupy your mind positively and keep away the dreaded boredom!

My advice here is, please don't rise to daft challenges or games just to try to find something to do, find something constructive that actually mirrors your interests and who knows? you might not be bored for too long!

Another big problem for people with ADD ADHD is bed boredom, and not in a sexual sense I would hurriedly add. That's not a problem I'd care to discuss here! However, sleeping patterns for people with this condition can be a real, erm… , *nightmare,* not really true here of course, as usually it's a lack of sleep that's the problem! When you are suffering from insomnia it's near impossible simply just to lie in bed, and this is when bed boredom strikes. Those with ADD ADHD may need to get up and do something active, though this is where a new problem might arise, as internet addiction may ensue, something that most people with ADD ADHD may recognise. Being bored in bed can lead to all sorts of problems that normals don't display and this will be covered further in the "red or black" section of the book.

These days, if I'm bored and can't sleep in bed I might make myself a good old cup of tea and start to write, eventually I find I will become tired and then it's possible to go back to bed and sleep. Of course, this can cause problems for those in full time employment who may need to rise early, as getting back out of bed at all hours of the night can prove to be a big challenge in itself.

Remember that the key to occupying your mind when bored is to make sure that you are doing something constructive and not just doing a thing for the sake of it. If your particular buzz is similar to the cases I describe, you'd do well to remember you may live to live to regret your actions - or indeed, may not.

Obviously everyone has a problem with boredom at times but it affects those with ADD ADHD a lot more than others as they will not have the ability to let the insignificant or trivial occupy their minds in the way those unaffected might.

In short, some of the things that 'normals' find interesting just don't do anything for people with this condition.

10. It says don't touch!

...especially on hot surfaces in chip shops, right! Yet how many of us have left a piece of our chin stuck to the silver shelves with the food on display? How many of us have burnt our fingers on something, just to see if it really is hot? and how many of us didn't touch the hot surfaces? not many at all, I'll bet!

This section will aim to demonstrate that telling a person with ADD ADHD not to do something, no matter what, just doesn't work. Even as an adult who is very aware of typical aspects of my condition, I still struggle with this one. I find I will still think twice about doing things that I'm told not to! And I don't think this will ever go away either, I'm afraid to say!

So how do we deal with this problem? Firstly, we have to find a balance between satisfying the urge to do what you are told not to with the self-interest of managing actually to do it and not damage yourself in the process! As you get older and the self-interest (others would term this, 'common sense'!) starts to take hold, this becomes much easier to do! If a scaffold says, "keep off - danger" anyone with any of this common sense will most likely just stay well clear and not climb the scaffold, simple! But I'm afraid it's not so simple in younger life, and quite often kids get hurt doing something exactly *because* it tells them not to. The sad thing about this is that if they weren't warned to keep off, there wouldn't be any urge to climb it. The sign might as well say, "Don't think of a giraffe!"

Any 'normal' reading this section might well struggle to relate to this, but for people with ADD ADHD I'm willing to bet you have bells ringing after reading this part!

Is this the reason why we are so bad at paying bills and filing tax returns, etc? Because we are told to? Maybe if we were told not to pay the bill or not to fill the tax form in it might actually get paid and get filled in? But somehow, I don't think so!

While the last example is obviously something of an exaggeration, we all know how bad we are at doing things we are told to, yet why is this so? We are so much better at doing things we are told not to! This is a baffler that I certainly cannot answer, unfortunately. If the hot surface in the chip shop didn't say "hot surface, don't touch!" there would be no appeal to touch it whatsoever and there would be one casualty less, as we know that we would recognise and fear the consequences. Another case in point is the good old dare! In my experience, you will struggle to find a person with ADD ADHD who will not rise to the challenge of a dare and this will be covered in greater depth in the "It's not big and it's not clever" section of the book.

I lived for four summers in Ibiza with people with ADHD in an effort to learn as much as possible about the condition. I found the experience very enlightening, and examples will appear throughout the book.

If my mate Yannis wanted me to pass him something, most often because he couldn't be bothered to reach it himself, he would resort to daring me to, for example, "pass the salt", knowing that it represented a dare I just couldn't refuse. There's a little tip for you if you want to get someone with this condition to do something for you! Another is to tell them that they can't do something, though they will get onto this one a lot sooner than the previous example.

Basically we don't do as we are told, can't do what we are asked, but are more than capable of doing what we are told not to! This is just another problem people with this condition have to go through each and every day and as this story unfolds you will see a many more situations that are just like this one!

Another common saying you often hear that fits in here is, "if he told you to put your hand in a fire, would you?" Teachers, particularly, have a morbid liking for this question, for some reason. The obvious answer is, probably not, yet if he dared you to put your hand in the fire the situation might well be different and you just might, as odd as this may sound. Remember here to know your boundaries and don't do silly things just because you are told not to or are dared to, it can easily end in disaster! Trust me on that one!

The title "It says don't touch" should apply equally to married persons, too. People with ADD ADHD on the whole have a big problem with this! Affairs are quite common in ADHD marriages and this without question adds to the divorce rate! If it says don't touch, just don't touch it... easier said than done when living with this condition!

11. Stimulate the Brain

I have mentioned previously in the book that boredom can and will often lead you down the wrong path and sometimes can land you in very hot water. Stimulating the brain in cases of ADD ADHD is a very important part of learning how to deal with the condition and a very good way of uncovering exactly what your hyperfocus button is!

Whether it be playing with a Rubik's cube or playing with a clothes peg, your conscious mind is occupied and whilst it is occupied you will devote a lot or possibly all of your attention to the action in question. Obviously, once you have completed a task like the Rubik's cube it has ceased to occupy the attention and as such probably won't be touched ever again. The clothes peg, however, is totally different.

I have sat and witnessed Yannis, for example, play with a clothes peg for hours, and have myself sat and played with a piece of bluetack for hours also. How can something so simple occupy the complicated mind of a person with ADD ADHD? I afraid I don't possess the definitive answer to this and I'm equally sure this doesn't apply to everyone. My own guess would be that these involve very tactile sensations, and as such appeal to the "hands-on" approach of the kinaesthetic learner. Some prefer to term these kinds of actions merely as 'fidgeting' and indeed, maybe they are. To these people I'd suggest that by fidgeting with things you may sometimes find new things of interest to you and you alone! Moreover, you may never even have known you had them!

This is where I would like, if I may, to introduce sport and music into the equation. How many people with ADD ADHD are massively talented at these disciplines, even where they take to them very late on? The answer is a lot and I myself know many personally.

I was at one time a professional rallycar driver and I am currently involved in the music and entertainment industry. I can vouch for the fact that the amount of people in all these areas with the condition is literally off the scale, and the natural talent involved here is immense!

I currently live half the year in the Isle of Man and half the year in Ibiza, and although the percentage of people with ADHD is very high on both islands, the number of super-talented people they play home to is quite extraordinary. I have found a massive connection with this condition and islands (see the Islands section of the book) especially when it comes to music, sport and entertainment.

Playing a musical instrument is a great way of stimulating the brain and some people find their "zone" whilst doing this. Some of the best musicians that I work with every day of the week have ADHD, diagnosed or not, and can play like I've never heard anyone play. However, approximately only 25% of them can actually read music! This totally shocked me, but seems to suggest that the naturally-gifted aren't necessarily the most conventional when it comes to learning. And yet they continue to be stigmatised by a supposed mental condition?

Another great example of this form of learning is sport. I personally know five World Champions, who all started quite late, most have largely taught themselves and yes, they all have ADHD!

Do we discern a pattern here yet? Many if not most of the really talented on the face of this planet have ADHD and that is a fact that will be proven as time goes on - yet how many go unnoticed?

By stimulating the mind and trying new things you might just discover that you could end up being one of the best in the world at whatever discipline you fall in love with!

I personally have always had a desire to be the best at everything I do and find that the major thing that gives me that drive and motivation is my condition. How strange that kids are still being labelled disruptive and excluded from school when potentially they could be among the most talented on the planet!

Don't be afraid to stimulate your brain and don't be surprised what you might find!

Some 'brainteasers' may not stimulate the brain of a person with ADD ADHD, they might only bore them and in fact do more harm than good. A classic example of this would be the crossword, and other academic puzzles, which are unlikely to interest people with ADD ADHD.

Give them a computer game and see what happens! (see next chapter)

And don't throw away the clothes pegs!

12. Computers and Games

This section follows directly in theme from the previous one of stimulating the brain. So often it is said that kids should not play computer games but in all honesty I'm afraid this is something that I totally disagree with.

It is very obvious how short the attention span of a child with ADD ADHD will be yet when they play a game, especially a computer game, they seem to be able to concentrate far more easily than 'normals'. This is because of what I call 'the hyperfocus button', as previously mentioned, and it really comes into its own as you get older and learn how to deal with your ADD ADHD. This isn't a tool that you have in your box as a child, although signs of it can appear from a young age.

It is very hard to attempt to train a very young child how to deal with ADHD but is very possible that children as young as 7 or 8 years old can be groomed to cope with their condition/gift. In the meantime they need to stay out of trouble! What better way than a good old session on their preferred console to occupy the mind? There are a good many positives to be had for the ADD ADHD child in terms of accomplishment and self-worth. I apologise at this point to any parents who don't agree with me on this, as there may be many other alternatives for kids with a regular attention span. Kids may say, "come on dad" before thrashing them at football or something. Well, it's largely the same with gaming. Beware though, mum and dad-once you start, you just can't stop! The only negative I can give about gaming by the way! It can admittedly become very addictive, and naturally you have to strike a balance. Only you can decide how long your child should play for optimum benefit, but extra time on the computer can be given as rewards for good behaviour with kids with ADD ADHD. Please don't deprive your kids of this as an option because you are old fashioned!

It's a fact that, not only is a child home and safe instead of getting up to potential mischief in unfamiliar surroundings, they are also learning things, stimulating their brains and sharpening up their reflexes. Very many parents think gaming numbs the brains of children, when in fact the reverse may be true! I would contend that it can be one of the very best ways of stimulating the brain, one which may benefit them in real-life situations! Obviously you must take care to ensure your children are playing suitable games, but this is very much your choice and no-one else's. Some of the games these days are very educational in specialist fields, too, and can actually teach amazing life skills. Ask yourself: how many top professional jobs these days rely on simulators for training? Some of the modern flying games are exactly like flying a plane, and are used extensively! And as an ex-rally driver I can attest to the fact that some of the driving games are virtually the same as real-time rallying, obviously with the added bonus that you won't get hurt when you crash!

I had four games cubicles in the internet cafe I had, and would say even then they brought the ultimate real-life experience that some modern games seek to capture. I don't subscribe to the theory that playing games lead invariably to mass-murder, though it may be wisest to choose your child's games very carefully! You will find that they find their own playing fields, and quite often something that they choose to play will interest them in real life, educating them in that field in the process! Usually someone who enjoys football will also love playing football on a gaming console but we must face up to the truth that even the most placid child will very likely enjoy fighting games, even where they have never had an argument in real life. Perhaps this is a form of release and parents should be aware of the good this might bring, instead of presuming their child might be about to go out and start doing kung-fu on passers-by!

On the other end of the scale there's now a good choice of games for even infants and they are more directed at teaching everyday education in a fun, colourful and interesting way, little different to standard Childrens TV channels.

Remember that children with this condition usually absorb knowledge slowly as they only learn from what they find to be of interest. This isn't to say that you will be in some way tricking them into doing school work by gaming, but there's definitely a massive platform here for a child with this condition to not only play fun games, but also learn a lot in the process! My suggestion is, give it a whirl! But be careful you don't get hooked yourself!

Anyway, enough writing for tonight! I'm now ready for a couple of hours playing PC games and stimulating my scattered brain in one of the ways I know best!

13. It's not big, and it's not clever!

The good old show-off must be centre of attention whether entertaining people or just making a downright idiot of himself in front of all and sundry. I have spent all my life doing all of the above and usually I have found to my cost that, at the time when you think you're doing something great in real life, in fact it's far from that. We all know that people with ADD ADHD get their best buzzes off doing things that they shouldn't do and will quite often push the envelope or try to take everything to the next level, especially if someone has just upstaged them in some way. This can become a very dangerous game to play, with often dreadful consequences.

A simple of game of dares can be fatal to persons with ADD ADHD, as they quite often have trouble knowing when to stop. This is frequently carried on into adulthood and is often the way that these people go on to prove to be so creative, but I would advise you not to use this creative talent just to do something dangerous and daring to impress your friends or whoever is watching.

People with ADD ADHD are among the most competitive in the world and will push everything to the boundaries to win things or to impress people! I once rolled over a car just for the sake of showing off to girls and because my mates were egging me on, as they often do! Looking back now I find it hard to believe I did this, though at the time it seemed like a really clever thing to do. This serves as a good example of the need to know the limits when it comes to showing off: it never crossed my mind that I or others might get hurt, nor did I think of the cost of repairing the car, just like I never took into account how we were to get home, or more importantly of the consequences to anyone else. This was a time when for sure I went too far, but there's another example here that I'm glad to say doesn't apply to me.

As I've stated previously, I spend each summer in Ibiza and when I witness the way that some of the English tourists (and there are lots, of course) behave it really saddens me. This summer alone more than ten English guys died falling from balconies and this is an all-too-familiar story, I'm afraid. Of course they didn't mean to fall and die but I'm afraid when alcohol or drugs, a summer holiday, a big drop, and girls on the next balcony are involved this is a toxic mix, and a total disaster in the making. I really shouldn't need to spell it out any clearer...YOU ONLY HAVE ONE LIFE!! Don't throw it away trying to impress people, or by trying to make someone laugh, or worst of all, just trying to win a game of dares!

There are lots of different examples of being not clever when it comes to the effects of this condition. It might also be the reason why so many of us excel at dangerous sports, the fact that maybe we don't care as much as we might, maybe we do not think about getting hurt and the fact that when up against the 'normals' especially when it comes to motorsport, they really don't stand a chance! I'm yet to meet a top bike racer who *hasn't* got ADD ADHD, especially the ones that race around the famous TT circuit on the Isle of Man. Some of the top guys' average speed for just one lap of the 38 mile road circuit is over 130 mph! There is nothing 'normal' about these people! Yes, they are loud and proud and often flamboyant, but they are nearly all people who most certainly have ADD ADHD, and probably know nothing about it!

Maybe after reading this book a few more of them will start to understand why it is they can ride a bike so much faster than their 'normal' competitors! This is a time when it *is* big and clever to show people what you can do! The more research I do, the more convinced I become of this pattern, of how people with this condition are so incredibly talented: they just have to find that talent to unlock it and, if you're anything like me, you will probably find it lies in something that you never considered before. Strange!

Your impulsive personality will always try and take over in any situations that arise, especially one that involves showing off to interested third parties. What you have to do is dig deep, call on our friend William Power and learn when enough is enough, before you get yourself seriously hurt!

14. You've changed!

Sometimes life gets to a point where if you don't change something, things will probably change for you, and usually for the worst.

Those with ADD ADHD can quite often be their own worst enemy and have a great talent for destroying not only their own lives, but those of all the people around them as well. Likewise they can be very easily led by those around them. You will always prefer to listen to your own inner voice and usually won't take notice of anyone else until something is suggested that seems a little more interesting to you than what you are currently doing! This is where you need to learn how to change!

As has been said, once you have accepted that you have the condition, then and only then can you learn how to deal with it. Remember that 50% of the 'cure' lies in knowing and accepting that you have a condition in the first place.

If you are dealing with it correctly you will notice yourself changing over a short period of time and more importantly others will notice a change in you! One bit of good advice: unless your friends are being positive about "the new you", ignore them! Indeed, I can only suggest changing your friends in such a situation! Have you ever thought that it might actually be a good thing that you *don't* fit in anymore?

Here is a great example: I have just been to the pub to watch England beat Spain 1-0 at football and now I'm sat at home on the couch about to have a wonderful meal with my wife. She's happy, I'm happy, and everything is set up for a nice quiet romantic night. Now, in the past going to watch a football game in the afternoon would have meant one outcome, that is, getting home late, probably very drunk and therefore almost certainly in the doghouse with my wife. Win or lose in the game it was in real terms just an excuse to go out and get drunk, then to go clubbing, and before you know it, you're getting home next day on the verge of divorce! You may think I exaggerate here but believe me when I say it happens all the time, and you might get away with it a few times, but eventually the wife will get fed up and she will be gone!

People displaying ADD ADHD go through on average 2.6 marriages! Impulsivity and addiction problems are a complete recipe for disaster when it comes to relationships and we are generally blind to the damage that we are causing around us. The only way to break the mould and beat this statistic is go through a process of change. It really is as simple as that!

It's not so bad after all: find something else to occupy your mind instead of going to the pub drinking, if that's your particular problem. The way I've changed myself is, I'm now sat here writing with a beer, but-hey - I'm not in the pub with a beer! Look at it as broadening your horizons, and maybe something you write might just end up in a film or a book and, who knows, you could even earn some money from it!

Aha, now that's got you thinking, hasn't it? People with ADHD generally have amazing imagination and can create some incredible things from nothing but a good idea and a bit of graft!

If you read the above and think I'm talking rubbish you have only to ask how you come to be reading this book. Because the person who wrote it decided one day to write a book about his condition, and the way that I am comfortable doing it is to write a section depending on what has happened to me that day! I came home straight after the football remember, and now I find myself writing before I have my meal.

Oh my God! Look how I've changed! But I console myself that I really do feel a whole lot better for it, believe me! Remember if you are prepared to start with yourself, then your life can change for the better, and in a very big and positive way!

That's just good old "positive thinking", and by the end of this book you will probably be sick of hearing the words! But this is the key to mastering your ADD ADHD. If you are positive about your changes I can assure you that your life will get positively better! However, if you are negative about the changes, well then that's just another excuse to give up and go back to being the old you, and only you will know if the new you or the old you is better! When you start to think negatively, you will begin to hate yourself and will very likely "fall off your wagon", so to speak - I don't mean that in the usual context of drink and drugs or suchlike, it purely means you will lose track of your recovery and go backwards in the fight to master your condition! Always remember there's a big prize at the end if you succeed! Anyone who learns how to use their ADD ADHD to their advantage and learns how to use the "hyperfocus button" has a great chance of becoming successful so stick at it! It will be worth it in the end, I promise!

15. Wasn't Me...

This section is intended as similar to another later in the book about living in denial and the reason I have deliberately included two so similar is to highlight the importance of the issues contained therein.

What is the first thing a child says when parents ask the question, "what are you doing?" The reply is nearly always "nothing", as I'm sure you already knew. One thing that stands out to me about people with ADD ADHD is that they are consistently very good at getting themselves out of trouble. Is this because of the amount of practice they have had whilst growing up?

Well, quite possibly, but there's also another good reason...because of their willingness to try new things and push the boundaries of life, they are very likely to end up in a spot of bother and their initial reaction is instinctively to try and talk their way out of it!

I clearly remember playing a "wasn't me" trick on a friend in school. He was sat by the main power switch in computer class, which operated all 32 computers in the room. For no particular reason, I persuaded him to unplug the switch, promising that if he got caught I would take all the blame if it looked like he was going to get in any serious trouble. Always the clown and the joker, always looking to take it to the next level! A few minutes later there was a flash, and all the computers in the class not only turned off, but erased all the work stored on them (this is going back 25 years by the way!) The teacher went berserk and looked straight at my pal sat by the main power switch and bellowed, "was that you Higgins?" My friend hesitantly replied, "no sir, it was Scott". I just started laughing and declared, "wasn't me, I'm not even sat by the switch!". It seemed obvious to the teacher that Higgins was guilty, and he was swiftly marched to headmaster's office whilst the rest of us erupted with laughter. Reading that back again makes me feel slightly guilty, but it's another example of how the mind of people with ADD ADHD can work at times: they are always looking for the ultimate laugh but don't like getting into trouble themselves, hence the reason they are so good at getting out of sticky situations. The natural ability to think outside of the box is a massive asset with this condition and very useful for getting you "off the hook" in certain circumstances (but only if you're cute about it!).

Research suggests a very high percentage of criminals have ADD ADHD and this I believe is why the police have such big problems convicting people from organised gangs, the likeliest group to re-offend. These people know literally every trick in the book, and every time the police do catch up with what they are up to, they have this incredible ability to change things round and move to new pastures; the criminals are always one step ahead of the police - no matter what the police try and tell us!

The thing I can remember about jail is that, unsurprisingly, you get to spend lots of time talking to criminals, and the amount of things you learn on how not to get caught is unbelievable. This is the reason why so many people re-offend, as after this learning process they think they now have the knowledge to get away with it, but these are merely the clowns, apt to listen to others and use out-of-date ideas which result in arrest! The clever ones take everything they hear on board and then add their own individualistic twist to things and before you know it, they are likely to have created the perfect crime! Most of the criminals that I have met in my life have actually been highly intelligent individuals and they always take care to have their lackeys to do their dirty work! This has been the way things have operated for years and will continue to be forever in my view: the clever ones will always find a way of being able to say, "wasn't me!" and the lackeys will always be left to pick up the time!

16. Tantrums, Temper, Temper.

Maybe this is the one section that both 'normals' and people with ADD ADHD will relate to, as it deals with something that every human has experienced at some point in their life. The difference lies in how often tantrums happen, as any family member in an ADHD household will know only too well.

The stress that these tantrums put on parents is massive, but don't forget what the person 'throwing the toys out of the pram' might be going through. Yes, this is a lot more apparent in children with ADD ADHD, but it does carry on into adult life and it's only through experience of situations that more adult tantrums are prevented.

I know from my own personal tantrums that the most trivial of situations is enough to send a child or adult with this condition over the edge, and the problem is that 'normals' just put these down to 'bad' behaviour. When a family knows that there is ADHD in the household it is much easier to deal with the tantrums, as they will know better how to diffuse the situations as they arise, or to prevent them from occurring altogether. As in everything, prevention is better than cure, so if an outburst can be avoided then that is obviously the best option. So often the smallest tantrum can break into a massive full blown argument and can escalate further from there as well! A good real-life example of this happened to me: I had stormed out of my parents' house, got into my car and set off at full speed. Unfortunately, I was in reverse and sped straight back into next door's brand new Audi causing many thousands of pounds of damage. As in all of these kinds of situation, I was instantly full of regret, and if only I could have either calmed down, or been calmed down, then the situation might never have happened! Anyone with ADD ADHD knows full well that they are not likely to listen to others so really, the only option is to calm yourself down!

How do we do that, I imagine you asking, well it's simple…get yourself in your personal zone - mine is in the car as it happens, but anywhere that makes you feel comfortable is fine. Some people resort to music, some may go for a walk, others will draw and so on. If you can get yourself into your comfort zone you will find that you can quite often calm yourself down and avoid harming others in a tantrum that probably should never have happened anyway!

In the case of tantrums in children it's not quite so easy to find the solution, but one thing's for sure with ADD ADHD, rewarding good behaviour goes down much better than punishing bad behaviour, and where there's bad behaviour, there's nearly always a tantrum.

My youngest son is only two, and obviously has inherited this condition, and when he throws tantrums it quite often scares me, despite my familiarity with all the symptoms! I have recently seen him go into a full blown panic attack because he didn't get his own way. Obviously, because of his age it's impossible to teach him how to deal with this on his own, so it's always down to the parents to figure out the individual situation for themselves with kids this young. As your children get older, and if you are honest with them about ADD ADHD, they might just be able to control these tantrums themselves and if they can do it as teenagers then they will be able to do it in adulthood.

It will probably be apparent by now that I'm a firm believer that education is better than medication for this condition, and although there will always be extreme cases where medication may prove beneficial, on the whole I strongly believe the less drugs kids are given, the better.

Where tantrums occur in teenagers and young adults, these may become much more serious, and so can the situations that we may find ourselves in. In no time a minor situation can turn into an argument, from there into a possible fight, and before you know it, you may have landed yourself in a young offenders unit or, as you get older, even jail! The percentage of people with ADD ADHD in jail is not surprisingly very high, and once you have been there it is very hard to get yourself accustomed to normal life without making a few more trips back!

This will be covered further in the "do not pass go" section of the book. So many of these people in jail are there because of assault convictions and fighting, and the main reason for this is because they find it difficult to control their temper and when provoked there is always only one likely outcome.

Make no mistake, people with ADD ADHD are often very much hardened individuals who have spent much of their childhood battling everyday life, and as a result are wont to tackle any given situation with the same gung-ho approach that they are accustomed to using! If you'd care for my advice, don't pick a fight with someone who has this condition, as it's quite likely you will end up on the losing side…and even if you win, there's a damn good chance they will be waiting for you the next day!

Another piece of advice I might give is that when a person with this condition does actually flip, there's a real chance that they will react in a much more aggressive manner than a normal person; you can quite often see a distinctive look in their eyes. In the past when in these kinds of situation, I have actually looked straight through people and it doesn't really register how big they are, strangely! Temper and aggression are two of the biggest downfalls of having this condition, and it's imperative to learn how to control this part of your life, because if you don't, you will inevitably end up in serious trouble at some point in your life.

17. Fun and Games

It doesn't matter if it's Hide and Seek or a plain old game of Monopoly, people with ADD ADHD just love playing games and are quite often the instigator in starting a game going.

We just never seem to want to grow up, and will be acting the clown for the rest of our lives - especially males. Even at the age of 40 I love messing around on shopping trolleys in the supermarket car parks, and if the opportunity arises to hide, then jump out and surprise someone, then I'm right at the front of the queue!

It's known that certain comedians have got ADD ADHD and in recent years some have gone on to design and host some of the best game and quiz shows on television today. Do you remember ever trying to get a game started out of plain boredom? Remember what some of the people you were with said? Does this ring any bells? "...I'm not playing" or "I'm not doing that, it's silly". This is what the 'normals' would have said! Maybe after some persuasion you might get them to change their mind, but they will always be hesitant, unlike a person with ADD ADHD, who would not only want to be included, but would also want to go first!

A good example regarding game shows is "Celebrity Juice", hosted and written by Keith Lemon. This man is, I reckon, one of the funniest men on TV, and my guess is he has ADHD, as indeed do the majority of the funny people that I know.

So there's another hidden talent attached to this condition, and it really isn't all doom and gloom when it comes to ADHD!

I have been fortunate to meet quite a few TV funny people lately and I can honestly say that in my view each and every one of them had ADD ADHD. What makes these people, who were by and large shy and quiet at a young age become these totally crazy funny people later in life? I think that they either adopt the attitude of "I really don't give a damn", or they have learnt to control their condition and now use it totally to their own advantage!

As I have said all along, people with ADD ADHD have the abilities to outshine 'normals' in every aspect of life (especially in the entertainment industry) but only if they learn how to control and utilise it, preferably from a very young age. It is time that this condition was looked on in a different way because without people around that are a bit mischievous and game for a laugh, there would be no fun and games and the world would be a much greyer and sadder place!

Boredom is a big factor in the 'fun and games' lifestyle, and who, as we have seen, gets bored so much more easily than the 'normals'? —obviously the people with ADD ADHD! But be warned! When it comes to playing any kind of game with people with this condition just take note how competitive they are and what they will do to win, even if it is only a game of tiddlywinks.

I have been in the process of designing a new board game for some time, and once my second film is underway - number one is currently in post-production - I intend to get back to working on it. Who, after all, would be the best person to make a mental board game that was daring as well as fun, and came in childrens and adult versions? A person who is slightly twisted, well normal in my world! There isn't a 'normal' person on the planet who could come anywhere near to a person with ADHD when it comes to inventing a new board game! I fully intend to take this game to the next level in every way possible and, as in my films, I want to get right inside people's heads and make the whole experience the best and most valid possible. The only way to do this is to push the boat out and this is something that I reckon I'm really good at!

Remember that you will always struggle to beat someone with ADHD as they have such determination, and one further piece of advice! When it comes to games, if there's a way of cheating, a person with this condition will be all over it!

18. You won't be late, will you?

The daily schedule, the hardest thing for anyone with ADD ADHD to adhere to. Eight out of ten people with the condition will either be late for an appointment or be so rushed that they end up totally flustered and stressed even in the unlikely event they do get there on time!

On paper the problems are quite easily prevented, but real life it is rather different. If you can't get yourself to work on time, what are the chances of you holding on to a full time job? They are very small indeed and this is where the worst statistic surrounding this condition comes into play. Fully 67% of people with this condition don't make it into the fulltime workforce!

When I was told this one I nearly fell off my chair in shock, but the more research I have done, the more I can see this to be likely. Obviously this isn't the only cause of the ADD ADHD - affected not being able to hold onto full time jobs for any great period of time but it is a massive contributory factor.

I'm afraid the same thing applies at school: if you can't get to school on time everyday, eventually you will end up getting punished, despite the fact that as we all know it is down to parents to make sure that their children get to school on time. What chance do kids have if parents are unable to keep a good schedule? Not much at all I'm afraid!

This is where a tested schedule/routine is the only thing that works when it comes to your children's school day! As an adult I try to plan as little as possible but when it comes to getting my kids to school on time then I accept you have to be prepared! How do we do this? It's quite simple in fact!

Little things like homework must be completed the night before the next school day, school bags should be packed and ready for the morning and the packed lunch also needs to be prepared the night before. At least if these basics are part of the everyday routine you will have a very good start to achieving this task that, so simple to the 'normals', isn't so simple to us.

Generally as a rule adults with this condition are extremely good at organising others but not quite so good at organising themselves, but luckily this means that the school run and the essentials that make up a school day are usually stuck to. No parent wants their kids to be late for school, and the only way of making sure this doesn't happen is by having a routine, I'm afraid!

Whilst at school and particularly in the younger years, the routine is very straightforward - when the bell rings you go to class, and when the bell rings again you leave that class, and so on.

This becomes a bit more of a problem in secondary education, as there is a lot more responsibility placed on the pupil to make sure he or she is on time and in the right place.

Special projects that teachers give children can sometimes cause problems, especially when the child is required to bring something to the school as part of that project. This is where parents need to help out a lot! If you have a week to get two toilet roll inners and some magazine articles for example, then start on the first day! Even as adults, those with ADD ADHD tend to leave things like this to the last minute, and this tends to cause panic and arguments that can easily be prevented by doing a little bit each day... "don't put off till tomorrow what you can do today" is a great saying that is so true to life for people with this condition.

If you can organise things correctly, there's far more chance of your children being able to organise things much better as they get older. I am now a fully grown adult who has mastered this condition but I'm sorry to say that being late is one of the things that still catches me out every now and again, and I don't mean because of bad traffic or similar, even though it is the top excuse used!! It's somewhat ironic that many people with the condition are among the worst at dealing with such behaviour, and hate people who are late to meet them. It's quite funny in a way, but I spend a lot of my life travelling to engagements and meetings where timeliness is a virtue, and although I usually manage to get there eventually, it is never without high levels of stress and much swearing and clock watching!

Really, you should always aim to leave yourself just that little bit more time than you would normally need! Don't put yourself under unnecessary pressure, as you will need to keep your stress levels to a minimum just to get through the challenging day that this condition brings!

19. The Naughty Corner

This, as they say, does exactly what it says on the tin! I found myself as a child spending a great deal of my school time in the naughty corner or stood in the corridor, or outside the headmaster's office.

Put simply, this is one of the oldest and still, in my view, one of the best punishments that seems to work for children, teenagers and adults alike. Adults? Well, yes! This is common practice within the penal system. Where a prisoner misbehaves whilst behind bars, they are still sent to a grown up version of the naughty corner, only here it is termed being "sectioned" or "sent down the block". Basically this entails being made to spend time totally alone and without any privileges, affording time to reflect what they have done that is wrong and time to calm down.

This very old fashioned form of punishment is still used extensively in everyday school life and, you may be surprised to learn, I use it on my kids as well! This is because, in my experience, when a person with ADD ADHD does something wrong they usually regret it straight afterwards, and that spell of time on their own is useful to give them time to reflect on their actions. Quite often my two-year-old son will go and stand in the naughty corner without me even telling him to, as he usually knows himself when he has misbehaved.

As we have established, one of the big problems children with ADD ADHD face is that they are instantly and without thought labelled naughty kids at school and this is one of the things that continues to disturb me. There is always going be an element of plain wrongdoing in every walk of life, but not all the transgressors have ADD ADHD, it's fair to say. Why, then, should school life be any different? Why should it alone recognise the misbehaviour, but not the underlying causes? After consulting a headmaster from a special school in the UK he confirmed to me that one of the biggest problems he faces is that kids that are naughty are instantly put in the ADHD bracket and more often than not don't even have the condition. This results in children that would benefit from the special education that's on offer sometimes missing out, as the genuinely naughty kids are given priority. This is all down to incorrect diagnosis and in my opinion, to lazy doctors! Giving a child with ADHD detention and more academic work that they obviously don't enjoy, and from which they have no hope of benefitting, is a bad punishment and quite often will make the child rebel even more! Leaving those of us either directly or indirectly affected asking, just when will the medical and educational professions learn how to deal with this condition properly? It has been around for about 170 years or thereabouts, so you might reasonably expect there would be better solutions in place for such children by now.

Far too many people still merely label these children naughty and proceed straight to the punishment stage, just making an already difficult situation worse. In the school environment it's a lot harder as the aim is to treat all pupils the same, but at home the naughty corner is a great solution to calming situations down without a massive punishment, as peer group humiliation isn't a factor.

The worse the crime, the more severe the punishment is not the best attitude to adopt when dealing with children with ADD ADHD, and where there is bad behaviour and punishment, it's important there should equally be rewards for good behaviour. When children with this condition do something good they should always be rewarded, it helps them to see clearer the difference between good and bad. I'll leave details on rewards and punishments to the experts and you can get all the advice and information you need about this from one of the kids ADHD books that I mentioned earlier. They contain good information on how to reward your kids with charts and bonus points etc. which you should find very useful.

Hard as it is to punish your children, it is something that is vital if you want their behaviour to improve. Ironic that as I sat down to write this, my son was being banished to his place of punishment. Whilst there was lots of momentary screaming and shouting, I knew that in five minutes he would be calm and perfectly okay again. To reiterate, this is a punishment which involves no hitting or scolding, no removing of privileges and, especially in young children, works very well indeed. It isn't this easy with teenagers obviously, and you may have to resort to taking away treats etc for this age group, as only at school does this seem to work at this stage.

Remember that the naughty corner is a punishment, so don't even think of giving them rewards when they have calmed down, as rewards are for good behaviour only, and not good behaviour whilst in the naughty corner. This is very important!

Section 2

1. Medication, or Education?

This has to be one of the biggest talking points when it comes to ADD ADHD in the modern world. I am definitely one of those people who doesn't agree with some of the current medication regularly being prescribed to children with this condition. Sometimes children as young as three are being given mind-altering drugs that are made up of class A and class B drugs!

I have personally witnessed a child taking one of these drugs prescribed for ADHD, and fifteen minutes later he was dribbling at the mouth and could hardly talk. He was, to all intents and purposes, basically a zombie.

I have always said ever since I started to learn about ADHD I see it totally as a gift and we are lucky to have it, as long as we have learnt how to control it, channel it and keep one step ahead of it!

Why would anyone want to take a perfectly normal child, who is full of creativity, and turn him into a zombie who can scarcely think for himself? I understand that in extreme cases there may be no alternative to prescribing some of these drugs but I certainly don't agree with the way in which they seem to be handed out willy nilly.

Over the last two years I have recorded a lot of videos that are now uploaded to the You Tube website (user name THETAPMAN100) and basically my aim was to keep a video diary of all the different stages of ADHD and how it affected me. These have since been used at some ADHD schools in the UK as the teachers found that the pupils were able to concentrate whilst watching them and in general they found them very helpful and interesting.

I believe that, invariably, education is better than medication, but this is a decision that you as parents will have to make after consulting your local specialist! If we are taught how to control the faults of ADD ADHD from a young age we will then still be able to fulfil our potential in the classroom and on into the real world! However, there are way too many side effects to the drugs that are given out, and some of them can be really nasty indeed.

An admission here: part of my method in writing this involves introducing details to the book as they arise, almost in real-time. I find this helps me raise these topics while they're still fresh. Tonight, as an example, I watched a programme entitled "My child's not perfect", and saw another only slightly naughty child placed in front of three doctors and - yes, we had the same old answer: "your child has ADHD, here is some Ritalin, see how you get on and we can alter the medication if you don't think its helping" I just don't understand how these specialists are not prepared to try a different approach? Can they, possibly, be in league with the pharmaceutical giants? It always seems to be Ritalin or similar and, even after the first tablet, I can guarantee you will definitely notice a difference in your child, who will have become akin to a zombie! It breaks my heart to see doctors handing out these potentially dangerous drugs after sitting with a child for five minutes!

There's little doubt that these drugs can be a massive help in the right situation, and although there is some debate about this, even I would have to agree on this count. But as I have said before, the problem is their being so freely prescribed, despite the proven side-effects.

I am not qualified to advise on these drugs individually but I have named the common ones that doctors are currently recommending and prescribing so that you can do your own research in order to then make your own decisions for yourself or your children.

Among the stimulants currently commonly in use are:

Ritalin; Dexedrine; Dextrostat; Focalin; Methylin; Adderall; Dexamphetamine and Concerta.

While some of the non - stimulants are:

 Capres; Tofranil; Pertofran and Autorix.

Please note that some of these are not available in the UK. My advice here would be to do your own homework and then discuss all of the above with your doctor or specialist, making sure to ask about the possible side-effects! Some of these can be nasty and can make your, or your child's, life change dramatically, and not always for the best!

Also, it would be a good idea to ask your doctor about coffee-yes, plain and simple coffee - as it seems to have good results without those horrible side-effects! Personally I don't want my children having suicidal thoughts at the age of eight, and I certainly have no intention of turning my kids into zombies either, so for me there's no doubt at all that education is better than medication.

Again I say: only you ultimately can decide what is good for you and your family!

2. ADHD: Tell-tale Signs

   This section will hopefully prove quite helpful if you are trying to work out if either yourself or a family member, or even a friend, have the condition. These are not doctors' terms incidentally, so there's a good chance you will be able to recognise many of these tendencies in your everyday life. The more of these you think fit your life or situation, the more chance there is that you could well have this condition, but to get a full and professional diagnosis you will always need to go and see a specialist.

DO YOU, OR ARE YOU, ANY OF THE FOLLOWING?

Get most of your thrills from doing something either out of the norm, or something unusually exciting and often dangerous?

Can't stand being told what to do, and have very little respect for rules and authority.

Think totally out of the box...a lateral thinker.

Always willing to try new things and break the mould!

Love heading off on adventures, no matter how big or small.

Have an addictive personality.

Act on gut instincts and use your own intuition a lot?

Enjoy pushing the boundaries of life?

Highly strung and known to have a bit of a temper?

Find yourself often getting sidetracked and distracted?

Have you got the ability to think positive and turn your thoughts into actions?

Have you struggled with depression or anxiety in the past?

Do you have family members who have any of these faults?

Are very determined to succeed in life and love challenges.

Do you butt into conversations a lot?

Did you find yourself in quite a lot of trouble when younger?

Are you an amazing artist, craftsman or builder?

Are you a good team organiser and are happy only when in charge?

Do you, or have you in the past excelled at something?

Do you often hear voices in your head telling you things?

Do you talk a lot, often about yourself?

Do you dislike routine?

Are you keen to voice your opinion much more than others?

Do you hate being told what to do?

Do you find yourself getting bored very easily?

Do you often find yourself day-dreaming?

When you have done something wrong, do you feel remorse and regret almost instantly afterwards?

Do you enjoy the thought of revenge and like getting even?

Do you struggle to complete simple tasks in everyday life?

Are you always rushing around and running late?

Do you find that you can organise other people perfectly but really struggle to organise yourself?

Do you like a party? and are you often the last to leave?

Can you see yourself doing mischievous things?

Do you suffer from sex addiction or have a very high sex drive?

Can you play an instrument or do you have a passion for music?

Do you quite often doubt yourself and think you underachieve?

Are there days when you just don't want to get out of bed?

Are you the life and soul of the party?

Are you always up for a laugh and love joking around?

Do you hate having to learn something unless it's self-taught?

If you're told no!!...do you do it anyway?

Do you listen a lot but rarely take any of it in?

Are you sometimes accident prone?

Do you have an impulse to speak your mind most of the time?

Do you quite often put your foot in it and upset people?

There are loads more signifiers, but all of the above are good tell-tale signs of people with this condition, and if you recognise a lot of them as applicable to you I suggest you go onto the internet and take one of the ADHD tests you'll find there...don't pay for it, though, as there are plenty available for free.

After you have done the test online, then it's your time to make a big decision - should you go to a specialist, or just get on with life in the only way you know how? This decision is yours alone, but I believe that most people can conquer this condition simply by increasing their knowledge, and hopefully after reading this book you should be much better equipped for the task!

3. Advantages of ADHD

Please understand that some of the advantages cited in this section are somewhat double-edged, but taken as a whole are overwhelmingly positive!

1. The hyperfocus button... when you focus really hard, you can complete tasks in a fraction of the time that a 'normal' would.

2. You will have the ability to turn a bad situation around very quickly and to make the most out of bad situations.

3. If need be you can work for up to three days and nights, only stopping for minor snack breaks, but only if your task is of interest to you.

4. You are classed as "THE TOTAL HUMAN" in some of the books available to buy on ADD ADHD.

5. You are very good at positive thinking, and because of this you feel you can achieve anything.

6. You are usually ultra-creative, and enjoy having fun whilst you work - there are lots of jobs around for this kind of person.

7. You totally believe in yourself and more importantly, are very good at convincing others.

8. You will make a good team leader or even boss if you can learn to control your condition and put it to use.

9. You are a type of pedigree, who has the ability to excel in business and will push the boundaries to succeed.

10. You have a very high and very imaginative sex-drive, this just has to be classed as an advantage!

11. You have the ability to excel in something, maybe it's music, maybe sports or entertainment - you decide!

12. You will be ultra-competitive and will be able to turn your hand to most things.

13. Selling sand to the Arabs comes to mind - you will have a great ability to earn cash...when you can be bothered!

14. You will always strive hard to win at games, even if you do have to cheat a little.

15. People with this condition are usually quite hard people and very, very determined, I wouldn't argue with them!

16. You have amazing vision of things and can quite often picture them way before they have happened.

17. You have the ability to think laterally or "think out of the box", as it's known.

18. You will be very good at making decisions, and are not the type to dwell on things forever!

19. You have a great ability constantly to keep picking yourself up, ensuring that, in the end, you will get there!

20. At times you can be very funny! And, therefore, have the natural ability to make others laugh.

21. Entertainment with a capital E...if there's any acting or performing to be done, you will have good ability naturally!

22. You can be very argumentative, and this will come in very handy in your future years (this is also a disadvantage).

23. You will always set yourself big challenges and try your best to pull them off, this can result in big success!

24. You are miles more creative than a 'normal' human, and there are some big careers around for these types!

25. You will have amazing communication and leadership skills, and will excel at organising projects!

26. You might find yourself day-dreaming a lot, this is the place you might just find "the next big thing"...got to be a big plus!

27. You are also a good problem-solver, and very good at diversifying and going off-piste!

28. You will find that you will pass exams (but only just!) without putting any undue effort in!

29. When you do put maximum effort in, you find that you can achieve more than most people, in a shorter spell of time.

30. You will find that you like helping other people, and this is something that one day, someone will thank you for!

   Please remember that most of the above points only apply when you put in the effort, you make your own luck in this world and generally you only get back what you put in!

4. Compared to Normals

When throughout this book I refer to 'normals', I am not attempting to separate out people with ADD ADHD from normal society, and I'm certainly not in anyway suggesting one is better than the other, but with the use of the word so many times in comparisons I feel it makes sense to be worded this way.

There are so many situations throughout life where a person with ADD ADHD would react totally different to a person without the condition, and I think it appropriate to give this its own section, filled with everyday examples of such situations. Maybe after reading this section, 'normals' may have a better idea of how a person with ADD ADHD works both in the workplace and in humdrum, everyday situations.

The first example is the good old queue. A normal person will queue for as long as it takes, but the person with ADD ADHD, on the other hand, will either take one look at the queue and then leave, or queue for a short while and then leave with the intention of coming back at a later date. The ADHD individual doesn't cope well with queuing up for things!

Another good instance arises when pulling up to fill your car with petrol. The standard procedure when running low might be to pull in for petrol to make sure there is never any risk of running out, whereas a person with ADHD will drive right to the limit of the car running out and sometimes past that limit. For some strange reason people with ADHD hate stopping to get petrol - often most probably, because they are running late, or simply can't be bothered!

Example three is my personal favourite! The good old instruction booklet. The first thing a 'normal' person does when they have bought some new gadget is read the instruction booklet from cover to cover. This enables them not only to build their item properly, but also to use it to its maximum effect. Quite the opposite of a person with ADD ADHD, who will only look at instructions once they have hit a roadblock along the way. First, they must set about teaching themselves how it functions! Even then, usually not using half of the parts the item requires.

Example 4: paying bills. A 'normal' person will usually pay bills on time and there should always be enough money at the end of each month to be comfortable. A person with ADHD however, will not be this efficient and though the bills will be paid, it will very likely be in their order of priority and probably out of next month's pay packet! I've been here a million times myself and have found it's only as you get older that you can organise the financial side of your life!

Example 5: running late. This is one that I reckon will apply to so many of you. A 'normal' person always leaves plenty of time for their journey and is very rarely late for appointments. Quite the opposite of the ADD ADHD person who is always on the last minute, running to the bus, driving down all the shortcuts and nearly always being late or at maximum stress factor just to get there on time!

Example 6: It's good enough! The 'normal' person will finish a task in its entirety, especially where that task involves a lot of thinking. A person with ADD ADHD, however, will quite often get that task to the point where "it's good enough", or "that will do!". They will always look for shortcuts to the system and always try to find their own way of getting the task to a stage where they think it is finished, unless it's something they are fascinated by! In that case it will be quite the opposite, as they will use the good old "hyperfocus button" to complete the task in hand in a way like you won't have seen before!

Example 7: the short fuse! Even in very testing situations a 'normal' person will persevere until that situation is totally sorted. On the other hand a person with ADD ADHD will only be able to put up with it for so long before "throwing their toys out of the pram", as it were. Patience is something that people with this condition only have when their task is of interest to them!

5. Prevention is better than cure

Like any illness or condition, prevention is always better than cure but how do we prevent ADHD? If you speak to a doctor, they will tell you that the "prevention" takes the form of something like Ritalin or Concerta. I do not agree with this at all, I'm afraid!

These drugs may mask the condition, but do nothing to prevent it. I personally think also that doctors are giving out these drugs way too easily and they are not diagnosing people with this condition properly. It's as if they think that by doping kids up, the problem will just vanish, but I fear that it's not as simple as that.

Why would you want to "prevent" a condition with dangerous drugs when there are so many other, and better, options available these days!

Special parenting techniques, combined with education and maybe alternative medicine in some cases is definitely the way forward. I don't believe there are many parents in this world who would like to see their children filled with mind-altering drugs when there are possibly other ways of treating them.

It's like when a child is bored, they will moan and cry and we then have to give them something to occupy their minds and suddenly they are happy again, even if it's only for a short period of time. Prevention lies in keeping the child occupied; the problem and eventual cure in our reaction to the problem, even if this cure is only for the short term.

It's all very well when you are cured of a problem, but we all know that ADHD isn't something that is curable even if it is treatable: this is when we resort to the next best thing, which is obviously intervention.

You can only consult your specialist or doctor to get the advice you need on preventing this condition as best you can, especially in the very young years. What happens as the children get older is that they learn to understand how their own minds work and this is the point where I think it's good to start educating them about the condition.

Since I have learnt how to deal with my ADHD I have prevented myself from getting in many of the situations that I used to find so difficult at school and this is obviously through education and not through crazy drugs with massive side effects! It's all very well picking something up that you have dropped, but if you didn't drop it in the first place then you wouldn't have to go through the process of picking it up!

Similarly, if you don't get into trouble with the police in the first place, then you wouldn't have to go through the process of trying to fix the problems that you yourself have caused. These are both good examples of how prevention is definitely better than cure!

People with ADHD quite often steamroller into situations and they will then spend many hours fixing that situation, this can often be the case with refusing to read instructions or following the normal way of doing things. Truth be known, we could have prevented the situation that's occurring by either thinking about it a little more or listening to other people's advice before tackling it!

There are so many times in life that we wish we could have prevented something from happening, and having ADHD is sometimes like having blinkers on, as you just don't listen to anything or anyone at times. Try to listen, and you will learn much more and make many things in everyday life become a whole lot easier.

If a situation can be prevented, then it doesn't happen! This is so important in the life of a person with this condition. Here are a few more examples of conscious interventions which may help in prevention...

If you put petrol in your car then the chances are you will not run out and then have to mess around filling cans and walking back and forward to the petrol station.

If you don't rise to a situation then you won't have to get involved in the argument that follows!

If you don't drink too much then there's a good chance you won't feel so rough the next day!

If you build something properly, then it won't fall apart, and you won't have to waste time rebuilding it again.

If you put maximum effort into something, there's a good chance you will get the maximum out of it!

It's not just about preventing or curing a condition, it's also a question of preventing the things that can cause you harm or stress in everyday life! Try to think just a little first, and then act on those thoughts and you will find that you achieve much better results as life goes on!

6. The Zone

This is probably the most important place in the world for a person with ADD ADHD, and yet so many just won't have a clue what it is, until that is you have read this section!

"The Zone" is the place where everything is good and everything works, a place of peace where problems don't exist and everyone is the same; it's the place where you need to put yourself when you are in a bad place. It comes in handy for so many parts of the everyday life of a person with this condition and is a place where problems can be made to go away and you can return to the normal world with a totally clear head.

Everyone has a different "zone", for some people it may be accessed by listening to music or playing an instrument, watching a film, by time spent alone, working out in the gym or in any one of a thousand differing ways-mine lies behind the wheel of a car. The second I'm behind a steering wheel, not even necessarily moving, I feel totally at home, an equilibrium or control if you will that just doesn't appear anywhere else for me, and this is such an important place for a person with ADD ADHD to be, especially when things are not going too well!

The way my mind works when in my zone is semi-divine: I can think straight, solve problems a lot easier and most of all, it's the best way I've found of controlling the big pitfall of ADHD, the rages!

Instead of lashing out as a result of the smallest of things like so many of us find ourselves doing (I call them flip-outs) and either quarrelling with people or just generally making an idiot of yourself, place your self into your zone! You will be amazed how much it can change a situation that you find yourself in and how differently you can react! How many times have we all done things that we regret instantly afterwards? As I've stated previously, this is highly symptomatic of the condition. What I've found is, instead of reacting often on impulse to a situation, that by waiting and thinking about things just a little bit more, even if you simply visualise your "zone" it can change the place you are in and the outcome with amazing results.

Everyone will know what their preferred zone is, but I suggest you try a few different ones, don't always go with the first option as you ordinarily might, listen to another voice for a change! In this case, MINE! listen to what I'M saying here, and I promise you that you will see massive improvements in your demeanour very quickly indeed.

Nothing bad will ensue when you put yourself into your zone and if you bring something out to the real world from your place inside it, there's a good chance the situation on the outside will be a lot better too.

Headphones are another really good and really easy method to use also, and of course this can be done without leaving your front door. So many people with ADHD struggle to discipline themselves to sit and read books, yet almost everyone likes listening to music, especially through headphones! The cordless models allow freedom of movement, some even outside the house. I would recommend any smooth jazz or chillout tunes, for the ultimate in relaxation.

There are so many "zones" and so many times to use them to full effect. Sports psychologists and coaches insist their sportsmen and women always get themselves into the zone before competing and it can totally transform the performance they put in. Equally if they are not sufficiently in the zone there is every chance they will be rubbish!

So, you don't have to have just one zone! There may be days that are really bad, and just popping into your zone won't work for the particular problem that you are having at that moment, this is a good time to have other zones that you can either picture or even go to!

A good one that I have found particularly useful is, if I'm having problems with the car, simply to make sure I'm on my own. So often it's the people around you that cop for the bad mood that you are probably in! 'Normals' will very likely struggle to appreciate how important a zone is to a person with ADD ADHD but it's not about others, It's all about *you* when you feel like this and only you can sort each individual situation out in your own way!

Take this "zone" that most of us have found and start to use it in everyday life. Even seemingly insignificant situations may benefit from its use. So often with ADD ADHD a small situation can become a massive problem, but by remembering and utilising this strategy you will find this can be avoided.

7. The Centre of Attention

While we often hate to admit it, people with ADD ADHD do like to be the centre of attention, and this can come in many shapes and forms! "Bad Lads" have always been the centre of attention for all the wrong reasons but for some reason that's the way they like it. It can take a good few spells in jail and a lot of growing up before people start to realise that being the bad lad isn't the best kind of attention.

The office clown is another good example of how being the centre of attention isn't always a great place to be, as quite often the laughter is directed at and not with the "star turn".

I haven't mentioned the female with ADHD much in this book, and they are much less likely to develop the symptoms. In fact women are four to nine times less likely to be affected by ADHD. One bit of advice here, and it's directed at the males, females with this condition are the best fun in the world but they can also be a real handful, and sometimes should come with a "handle with care" sign stuck to them.

The trouble is that males and females with this condition are definitely attracted to each other, and it does lead to very fiery but very loving relationships! Almost always, females are more adept at being the centre of attention, as males most often just end up making fools of themselves.

One of the things that most noticeably affects the personality of a person with ADHD is alcohol. Many of the more compromising situations we find ourselves in do actually arise at times when we are drinking, as I'm sure you will have already found out for yourself! How often in the past have you spent the first half of the week apologising for things you have done over the previous weekend? And when you live on an island or in a small community as I do, it's not long till everyone starts to see a different side to you. Unfortunately, the side that they often see is the drunken fool who can't keep their mouth shut, who constantly butts in and is very annoying. Very different to the nice person that you know you are normally!

This kind of behaviour, even though at the time you may think it's funny, can take years to repair. You will find that you can make the most horrible first impressions on people. These first impressions last and they literally last for years - it can be very hard to change someone's opinion of you, especially from that first meeting!

It's not all bad news in this section though! Without the ability to become the centre of attention you will never be able to be a good leader or a good speaker in front of people and this is essential in the world of business and generally if you want to get on in life!

I have found from my own experience that instead of expending huge amounts of energy in trying to make a good impression, usually the wrong way and failing miserably, it's often better to pay that first meeting scant attention, and to end up becoming the centre of attention totally by accident - well sort of, it may be a little bit by design I suppose!

As I seem to be meeting some pretty important people in the creative field these days, I have to be extra careful. My adopted strategy is to let others grab the attention right up until a point at which I know I am comfortable and can take the current conversation to the next level without seeming rude or daft as a brush! It's more important than ever for me on a personal level to ensure that the people don't walk away thinking, "who the hell was that clown?" ...but how do you find the perfect balance between achieving your ultimate aim, which, let's be honest, will be to grab most of the attention to your best advantage, without appearing self-centred, or a bore? This is something that takes ages to perfect and if I was to be totally honest it's one of the things that I still have to consciously work toward, trial and error is the only way you can find your own limitations and when you do eventually find the perfect balance, just remember that with each drink you have, your judgement becomes a little more clouded and this is when disaster can strike! A bit like when a comedian tells the shit joke that silences the room, this is definitely the kind of situation to try and avoid at all costs, because you will find yourself the centre of attention for all the wrong reasons!

8. ADHD...Disability, or gift?

There so many advantages and disadvantages to having ADD ADHD but one thing is for sure, there's no cure, so one way or another we have to learn how to deal with it!

Some class it as a disability - in fact, in the USA if you have ADHD you automatically qualify for special education. Throughout this book you will see good things and bad things about life with ADHD, but the day that I admit to it being a disability is the day that I die! My research has found some amazing attributes applicable only to people with this condition and as so many of these are very successful individuals I wouldn't suggest that they are disabled in any way.

Admittedly we display a minor brain dysfunction which very obviously affects different people in different ways, but for all we know, we could have been made that way on purpose! Slightly different to everyone else and prepared to stand out that bit more, the ones who will always be trying to take the world forward...making everything evolve at a faster pace...or are we just the disruptive ones, who always have an opinion and cannot be doing with rules and routine?

"Normals" quite often look differently on people with ADHD and you can tell they feel threatened by us, as they don't like change-especially in the workplace - and as we have established, all we ever want to do is change things.

Take a look at the cross section of the following examples and you will soon see that it's not all bad news when it comes to ADD ADHD.

We all know that we talk too much, but is this not just an example of how passionate we are about different things? We definitely live life for the moment and although some would say that we are impulsive, I for one wouldn't want it any other way.

Apparently we have been known to focus on things that don't matter, however it could as easily be said that we find things interesting that others don't! Equally, while we find it hard to get homework done, isn't this just because we are so keen to play and interest ourselves, remaining active in a different way? And though we are considered hyperactive, surely this is a good thing as we possess a massive abundance of energy.

We are prone to daydreaming, but this can be where the best ideas come from and we can teach ourselves to relax well. Some may say that we are very selfish but I would say that we all know what we want and will do anything to get it.

Yes we have been known to butt into other people's conversations here and there, but isn't this an indication of our eagerness for others to hear our great ideas?

And of course we can lose things, but you will find that we only lose things that aren't usually that important...excluding keys, perhaps!

Some say that we ignore others, but personally I find myself guilty of this only where I feel that my own ideas are more advanced than theirs.

Yes we have been known to make mistakes, but so does everyone, and at least we have proven ourselves very good at correcting them!

Quite often we can upset others, but we always go with our instincts and this can only be a good thing!

We don't think before we act...this is true, but there again we have a great talent for trusting our gut feeling and intuition.

Admittedly we can be very annoying...but we are also the best when it comes to entertaining people!

Yes, ADHD causes big problems at school, but you will find that you excel a lot more than others after school is finished.

We are not that good at managing money...but we are certainly very good at making it, so no problem there!

We struggle to concentrate on one thing alone...but have the ability to do several things at once!

I think there's ample evidence to prove that ADHD can be a massive disadvantage, especially when you are younger but, as you go through life and as you learn how to deal with your condition, you will find yourself discovering many new talents, some which you could have never imagined! Personally I would rather have ADHD than not have it, and I sympathise with those of a different view, but I would stress the only reason I feel the way I do is because I have learnt how to handle my condition - well most of time anyway!

9. Normal in my World

That's what I keep telling myself anyway! ...and so should you! Yes, people with ADD ADHD are slightly different to 'normals', but that's not necessarily a negative! Constant bad press has led to people with ADD ADHD being labelled as naughty! And while this may be true, it's not that true!

In the research that I have been doing I have found that people with this condition are strongly attracted to each other, and there are many reasons for this. The main one being that they find many normal people just plain boring. I hate to say this, but I struggle to spend time with boring people, as they actually drive me round the bend! There's definitely a strong pattern prevalent in the Isle of Man and Ibiza which suggests that these people stick together and it's not at all uncommon to see two people with ADHD end up getting married or in a relationship. Obviously, when people eventually have a family, and because ADHD is 80% genetic across your whole family tree, there's a greater chance the kids will also have the condition and I personally believe this is why its incidence is so concentrated around islands.

As we're all inclined to gravitate naturally toward people that are similar to us we tend to think we that we are 'normal', and this is where I got the title for this section, "normal in my world".

Additionally, we spend so much of our time daydreaming that this often causes us to slip into our own little world. Personally I love inhabiting my own little world as it's a kind of an escape from the drudgeries of reality! People with ADD ADHD like to run or hide away, and this is a coping mechanism for the problems affecting us, I suspect. You need to start to teach yourself how to tackle things head on, but if you're anything like me, just a few minutes alone in your own little world or zone is the perfect preparation to tackle a big problem. 'Normal' people can't seem to relate to this as they look at daydreaming as something that maybe thick or lazy people do to spend their time! However I can safely say that most of my best ideas come from moments in my own zone, the one place where I can feel totally normal!

I also get this very same feeling just by spending time in Ibiza, every time I set foot on that island I start to feel like a totally different person and feel I can relax so much more easily when I'm there. Is the reason for this because so many people there also have this condition? Maybe that's something to think about, a place where everyone is a little bit different and yet all get on perfectly and feel totally normal in their world!

Maybe one of the reasons we didn't always fit in at school is because our normal world usually got us into trouble. I used to hate it at school when a teacher saw me daydreaming and then asked me what she was talking about - of course, I could never answer and usually ended up in the worst place in the world, detention. Detention is probably the worst thing you could give a person with ADD ADHD as it's designed to be so restrictive, we so hate being told what to do and being held against our will, plus we detest school and having to spend even more time there is the worst! Add to this torture the fact that we are not allowed to speak to each other, the one thing we all can't seem to stop doing. It's almost medieval in its barbarity!

Did you notice that most of the time you were in detention there would be someone sat next to you that was the same as you? How many times did you get told off for talking to each other? Why can't 'normal' people see what goes on in our world?

I remember once sitting with a group of BMX riders, all talking about some of the daft things that they had done, and it was eye-opening even for me, but if any 'normal' was sat there they wouldn't have believed what they were hearing. Yet to the BMX boys, such scary adventures were just totally normal in their world!

You only have one life! Don't spend most of it thinking you are not 'normal', whatever that means, just tell everyone "I'm normal in my world"!

10. Disadvantages of ADHD

It shouldn't be such a surprise if some of the disadvantages are in total contradiction to the advantages earlier in the book! This condition works in very strange ways indeed!

1. You could be labelled as someone with a mental condition, which can be quite damaging when you are younger.

2. You can be quite prone to trouble, especially when you are younger!

3. You will have a very impulsive behaviour pattern, and this can prove problematic.

4. You will have a problem with authority and struggle to respect anyone who thinks they are better than you.

5. Your mouth will more than probably land you in hot water quite a few times during your life, which may prove an understatement.

6. You will find yourself always doubting things, and this can hold you back a lot.

7. You will have a very addictive personality and you will find it hard to say no to certain things, big problems can lie ahead!

8. On average you will go through 2.6 marriages - people with ADHD can be very hard to live with.

9. You will get stressed out very easily, and you must learn how to control this, as much for your own health as anything else.

10. You won't have much in the way of patience, and in extreme cases you might walk off mid-conversation if someone is boring you.

11. You will struggle with many of the simple things in life, and will struggle to hold a schedule together, for example.

12. People with ADHD often have lots of different jobs over their career, and some struggle to stay in full time work, for reasons already outlined.

13. You will often beat yourself up over the most trivial of things, and you often think you are a failure!

14. You can often read way too much into situations and make a mountain out of a mole hill.

15. The smallest mistake or error can feel like a massive catastrophe, and failure can be devastating!

16. You will suffer from chronic inconsistency, and this can often lead to minor depression.

17. You will probably be very accident prone and pick up more injuries than is usual!

18. You will find yourself very distractable, and quite often drift off into a world of your own.

19. You will often get naughty urges! I'm not going into details as they will be very individualised, but trust me, they will happen!

20. You will often shout a lot - be aware, this never goes down well in modern society!

21. You will struggle to hold on to a permanent job, and hate keeping to a time schedule, two facts which go and in hand!

22. You will suffer from anxiety and depression, which can have devastating effects.

23. If you have ADHD, there's a very good chance you will also show symptoms of the other related conditions.

24. It is both lifelong and can be life-threatening, and causes major problems in the family household!

25. Drug addiction is a major problem with people with this condition, drugs providing that missing buzz on occasion!

26. You will get bursts of uncontrollable energy, especially in your younger years - this can also spell trouble sometimes.

27. At times you will find it very hard to sit still, and will frequently annoy others by your fidgeting.

28. Having ADHD can sometimes go against you when you are looking for a job, as employers often don't understand it.

29. Sometimes it can be a very lonely life for people with ADHD, especially when they have no one to turn to!

30. You can be very argumentative - though this point also appears in the advantages section, it must be said!

11. Has Anyone Seen The....

Is this the most-asked question in the world of ADD ADHD? I reckon it could well be, and it's certainly one that I use way too much in my average day! The really sad fact is that this is definitely one of the hardest things to train yourself not to do. In the summer in our mad house in Ibiza (a group of people with ADHD living together), the amount of times the above phrase was used was ridiculous.

One thing I did notice, the more so after doing it repeatedly myself, was several of us asking where something was whilst walking towards it! Why do we do this? Even the whereabouts of the kettle, which lives in the same place in the kitchen every day of the week, would be questioned, as we were walking towards it! Only later did it become apparent that not only did we all do this, but we all did it an incredible amount of times! Now if this is what we do when we know where something is, you might imagine what we are like when we actually can't find something we are looking for! My poor wife must have the patience of a saint, as she spends a large proportion of the day looking for things that I have mislaid!

When a person with ADD ADHD can't find something, it is very easy for them to fall into a mad panic and start running around while getting absolutely nowhere, very rarely finding what they are looking for. I seem to have spent half of my life looking for things, ok maybe a slight exaggeration but it certainly represents a lot of my life wasted, in my opinion. I do have some great tips that will help you if you stick to them and although these are things are very simple, it's usually the simple things that you can never find: keys, phone, and the list goes on! When it comes to keys, there are a couple of really good options, the first being a lanyard around your neck with the keys tied to it. You may think this is a bit OTT but believe me, you can't lose something when it's tied around your neck. Once you have removed the lanyard after arriving home, place the keys on your new key board that you will have purchased (the best 2 quid you will ever spend) and rest assured they will be there in the morning, and you won't have a stressful race around the house looking for them! If you stick to the above you will never lose your keys, so that's one problem solved!

Next come the accessories that you wear, especially in winter. Keep hats and gloves together at all times - how many times have you ended up with one glove to add your collection - people with this condition quite often lose things like gloves, but I'm sure you knew that already!

The list goes on to phones, TV controls and wallets etc, and the only way you will combat this problem of losing things is to make sure the basics of your life are in order. How do I do that? I hear you asking. Dead simple! Give everything its own home, phone and wallet might go in a drawer by your bed, the TV control possibly live on top of the television when not in use, and so on. Before you know it you will find that the only things you need to ask the whereabouts of are the new or obvious things in everyday life that you haven't managed to find a home for yet!

It is quite strange how people with ADD ADHD hate looking for things in everyday life, but give them a treasure hunt to compete in and they will probably win it! When looking for something is a big challenge or a game it becomes fun and that is what's needed to make people with this condition enjoy things. We all know that it's no fun looking for something that we have misplaced, but give us something to look for that has been put there by someone else or hidden, then the whole changes!

This condition makes us do weird things, but even as adults we love the thought of having to solve or find something, especially if there's a prize at the end of it! Remember not to get stressed when looking for things, and try to adopt my mum's motto for instances like this....less haste, more speed!

The buzz of finding something is way better than the stress of not being able to find it!

12. The Adrenaline Junkie!

People with ADD ADHD thrive on any kind of adrenalin buzz, and it's probably no surprise when you take into account what this condition is all about! ADHD is caused by a minor abnormality in the brain, and involves how much adrenalin your brain puts out at different times. I'm skipping the medical details obviously, because again, I'm not a doctor, but I will always aim to give you enough information to enable you to research the exact medical terms yourself. Why do we love the ultimate buzz so much? And more importantly, why do we feel so much better after a big adrenalin rush? Why can it make us feel a lot better when we are ill? I put all of the above to the test this summer in Ibiza and confirmed everything that I've always suspected!

One day I was feeling really low - a combination of depression, lack of motivation, a massive hangover and the dreaded man flu, quite a nasty combination to deal with! Normally, a day in bed would cure all of the above and you would just lose a day, but that's something that's not possible when filming, as we were. I decided instead to try something very different for a cure! I went down to the bungee rocket and got fired into the air at 100 mph and pulled about 5gs! This is one of those situations that will give you a massive adrenalin rush, in fact that's probably a slight understatement, but the end product will surprise you! After such an adrenalin rush all the sickness had gone, I was in a great mood and the depression was replaced with motivation! I basically felt like a new man and was looking forward to tackling the day ahead. A few days later I felt in a similar low state and decided to try something else a bit different to get the adrenalin rush. I fired up the scramble bike and went tracking for 15 minutes, basically enough time to break into a sweat and get the heart really racing and that good old adrenalin flowing. The outcome was the same as a few days earlier - I felt totally fine and 100 percent refreshed. After repeated tests on sick days throughout the summer we all came to the conclusion that this adrenalin rush definitely improved any sickness and massively helped us on the depressing days to lift the mood!

If we take all of the above into account, would it be possible to suggest that adrenalin might be one of the drugs that researchers and scientists should be looking into further for helping people with ADD ADHD?

Anyway back to the adrenalin junkie: the amount of people that I know with this condition that take part in extreme sports is off the scale! Whether it be skateboarding, BMXing, moto-cross or rallying, nearly everyone I've met who do the above sports had ADD ADHD, especially the ones who excel! I have started to discern a definite pattern and from that have built an opinion that most of the most talented sportsmen and women probably have ADD ADHD and this applies to normal, as well as extreme sports!

Down sides to being an adrenalin junkie are all-too apparent! Gambling gives a massive adrenalin buzz, especially when you win and it is well-known how easily people with the condition get addicted to gambling! Bedroom antics also provide a massive adrenalin buzz, but because you are always looking to try to take things to the next level, this is another rush that can land you in trouble! Another one is extreme sports - how often do you see your local moto-cross riders walking around in plaster? Quite a few, so if you're intending to do extreme sports to get the adrenalin rush that you need, just be prepared for the odd injury!

There are good and bad aspects to being an adrenalin junkie but, at the end of the day life is for living, and try telling anyone like us any different!

"Live every day like it is your last", has to be one of my favourite sayings and it probably will be the end of me one day...

13. Verbal Diaorrhea

Although quite often a little slow to start talking, once they start, people with ADD ADHD just don't seem to like to stop. In the past it was always me who was the one to talk but these days I get a lot of humour and ideas just from listening to people with ADHD ramble on about nothing in particular. Whilst living with several different people all with the condition I have experienced some of the funniest and more importantly, pointless arguments that have ever taken place!

It's not very hard to spot a person who might have ADHD incidentally, just listen to the person who seems to be talking the most and more than likely, talking about themselves. This is much more obvious in adults as lots of children talk a lot. Children with ADHD are definitely the worst at talking verbal diaorrhea, though! This really does stand out, and can be a huge problem, especially going through the education system. The rule in classrooms is that you speak when you're spoken to and only talk about the subject current in that classroom. Unfortunately for a child with ADD ADHD, this is easier said than done! The amount of times that I have been banished from class and made to stand in the corridor for talking is probably some kind of world record. Another massive problem arises when we are told to be quiet, as sometimes we get an even bigger urge not to comply, and this is ADHD at its most rebellious and one of the major reasons why we are classed as "naughty kids". Quite unbelievable that in the year 2011, some schools are still using ADHD as an excuse to get rid of their so-called naughty kids, which appalls me!

There is however one advantage to having verbal diaorrhea, so it's not all bad news! If you're good at talking rubbish, which we all have to admit we are, then there's a really good chance that you will be brilliant at talking about things you know about!

When it comes to public speaking we really are the mutt's nuts, as they say! I won the school public-speaking easily, but was also told off most for talking when I shouldn't have been!

When it comes to great leaders they are all amazing speakers, and can communicate and come across very well indeed. This is a massive gift and something which will come in handy all the way through your life should you be fortunate enough to be blessed with it. Having the confidence to speak in front of people is something that you will need to perfect if you are going to venture into the world of business, for example. If the boss can't talk properly then there's not much chance of the business really doing much at all!

Some comedians can be a classic example of a human being with the verbal runs - some of them just can't shut up, and when you combine this with some of the things they come out with you quite often see a classic example of natural talent with a difference. It takes a lot of bottle to be a stand-up comedian and it is something that I would definitely like to try in the future. It's obvious to me that all stand-ups have got ADHD, and in my opinion some have got something a lot more profound than ADHD. The term "nutter" quite often makes appearances throughout this book and I must admit it is one of my favourite words in the whole world! It is recognised in most countries and is the perfect word to sum up a person with this condition.

Use your head! And if you have got something that just has to be said, then say it, you can always deal with the consequences at a later date! You also have the amazing ability to talk your way out of situations as quickly as you got yourself into them. This is another very useful tool to have in the box!

14. I'll have some...what is it?

This is a saying that my mum says I used all the time whilst growing up. Always wanting a piece of what's going on, whether it be a cake getting cut up or gifts being given out, I always had to have my nose right in the middle of it.

As I have grown up and can now analyse my childhood, this is definitely one of those things that has stuck with me right into adulthood and the more I think about it, the more I realise it is yet another thing caused by my ADD ADHD.

Wherever there's a group of children that are asked to form a queue I can absolutely guarantee you that the ones at the front of that queue will be the ones with ADHD. It's as if they have to be first in line for everything, as though they are frightened that they are going to miss something. This is also very obvious when kids at nursery are playing with toys, they will always have their individual favourites and will literally run to make sure that they get the toy they are after. Just beware then, when a child takes a toy that another child is either playing with or wants to play with - this is when sparks can fly and arguments arise!

"I'll have some, what is it?" also applies to gossip, and people with this condition are always at the forefront for this. If it isn't gossip about themselves personally, this doesn't matter - it will be gossip about other people! Nobody likes a gossip, and this is a big problem for people with this condition right up to the point where they get themselves in trouble a few times because of it, when finally they might learn to mind their own business a little bit more.

The fact is, because we are always involved in whatever is going on, be it something dangerous or naughty, or just an old-fashioned chin-wag, the problem that inevitably ensues is that we just can't keep things to ourselves and end up passing on to others 'information' of sorts we have received, whether it be correct and truthful or just an exaggerated pack of lies! You need to teach yourself not to talk so much about yourself but maybe more importantly, you need to teach yourself not to talk about others. I have landed myself in hot water up to my neck on many occasions in the past but not recently, certainly not since I began to read books that taught me how to deal with this aspect of ADHD.

We are renowned - notorious? - for being people who talk a lot, in fact we talk way too much, and this can be a good thing when we are talking about something very interesting or something very constructive, but no good whatsoever if all we are doing is spreading daft and silly untruths about other people! This is much, much harder to stop doing than you might think, and it will usually take someone else to point it out to you before you eventually realise it may not be a good idea!

So, try to keep your nose out of things unless they directly affect you, otherwise you might get to a point where people just won't tell you anything for the fear that you will just spread it round to others that you know! I have lost friends and upset many people in the past because of this and it wasn't until I spent a little time in jail that I began to learn to keep things to myself!

You don't always have to see what's going on, just as you don't always have to be the centre of attention - let someone else play this role for a change, and let them be the ones that annoy everyone!

15. The Mistakes

Live for the moment *yeahhhh!!*, no regrets mate! This is one of the mottos of a person with ADD ADHD but in truth how many of us would turn the clock back just a little bit if we were given the chance? We seem to make a lot more mistakes than the 'normals', and the secret to combating this problem is to learn not to make the same mistake twice!

No-one, ever, stops making mistakes, but if you can learn to make your mistake only the once then obviously, you thereby reduce drastically the amount of mistakes that you make!

I have made one very big mistake in life and it cost me my rallying career and it took nearly seventeen years to find a little bit of success again. So many people don't ever recover from their unnecessary mistake, so I'm very lucky to have another bite of the cherry as they say!

Once I found out I had ADD ADHD I started to realise why I had made some of the biggest mistakes of my life, and while I wouldn't use it as an excuse, if I had known then... (as they say), I am certain my life could have been so much easier and now I'm in control of my condition I'm really looking forward to the future, still making my own mistakes but ensuring they're nowhere near as big as past ones! Life begins at 40, if the saying is to be believed, - well it does for me, I hope, but it can also be a lot different for you, too, reading this! I'm hoping this book will help prevent some of you making big mistakes that go on to ruin your life, as mine nearly did.

One good way to accept making mistakes is to acknowledge the fact that you will get an opportunity to fix many of them in the future. People with ADD ADHD will torment themselves with the thought of underachievement and failures in the past, I've done it myself!

One way that I have found of making myself feel better about my mistakes is by making a list of things to do before death. In this list of ambitious things are a lot of things that I didn't achieve or get right previously in life, and as I work through the list, each time I cross one of them off, I gain enormous satisfaction in the knowledge that it is a previous mistake corrected!

THINGS TO DO BEFORE DEATH

Make mum and dad proud.

Repay my wonderful wife for putting up with me.

Make two Ibiza films and a great gangster film.

Win the Isle of Man rally.

Have a baby girl to add to my 2 boys.

Make a film that gets nominated for major awards.

Buy a Harley Davdison.

Write a book on ADHD in the hope of helping others.

Learn how to Tap Dance.

Design and build my own house from scratch.

Try to help as many people as much as possible.

Have a number one best-selling film.

Have a number one best-selling soundtrack!

Learn to speak Spanish.

Defeat the urge to take revenge for everything that goes wrong.

Do a back-flip on a moped or a motor bike.

Make TAP a global brand!

Win a BAFTA award for one of my films.

Learn to respect others more than I have in the past.

MAKE A DIFFERENCE…SIMPLE AS THAT!

As you can see, I'm likely to be very busy, let's hope I don't make too many mistakes in the process!

Remember the phrase "everything happens for a reason"? Well, sometimes in the world of mistakes this can be a good get-out clause! You don't need to over-punish yourselves for making mistakes, so try adopting that phrase, you might find it helps!

16. Did You Butt In?

One of the biggest problems a person with ADHD faces is holding a conversation in the normal way. When referring to 'the normal way', I actually mean by letting the other person speak and then waiting a reasonable and respectful amount of time before responding - a two-way conversation, in other words.

Children with the condition can be especially annoying to others when they are constantly butting in, and I'm afraid that this problem isn't one that is likely to fade over time. I have had to train myself over the years not to interfere in conversations but every now and again I still slip up, often without even noticing that I'm doing it! The biggest problems in life can be those you aren't even aware of, and after all if you don't know you're interfering, how can you stop yourself doing it?

Can you imagine having to sit in at a meeting where you constantly have the urge to interrupt and speak? Right at this moment I am just about to start negotiating with some big companies to try to get the all-important cinema deal for my film. I have spent a lot of time going through what I'm going to say in my head, as these meetings are probably the biggest I've ever had in my life. I know that if I get the right distribution deal, the film could turn a healthy profit. As the stakes are so high, I have been training myself to listen much more intently and to try and note my points down on paper. This way I know I can deliver all of my questions at once and not come across as interrupting in a rude or untimely manner, or at least, this is what I'm hoping. If I was to be totally honest, this is the first time I've tried this method, as I usually go in 'all guns blazing', so to speak! I know I'm going to really have to discipline myself in these meetings however and only make my points when it is absolutely essential...nobody likes an adult that butts in, just as no-one values this in a child, but the advantage in adulthood is you might just have the knowledge or the idea that makes you look extremely cool when you butt in... are you one of these very rare breeds of people? My guess is, of course you are! It's another one of the secret abilities of those touched by ADHD. Another area that seems to attract people with ADHD is the legal profession. The barrister or lawyer has the ability to react very quickly to rapidly-changing situations, to think on his/her feet with great accuracy and precision, often interrupting proceedings to explain to the court their objections to or interpretations of facts as they are unveiled.

In short, a good lawyer should butt in all the time, as long as he isn't given to flights of fancy, then he/she will be very successful in his or her chosen field.

Politicians are another breed that need to possess the ability to make such interjections, but they in their case they don't yet seem to have mastered doing it without looking arrogant or supercilious.

Learn to interrupt in a timely and polite fashion, and make sure that when you do, you can back up your point with precise facts and statements. This is the only way you will ever be able to get away without risk of failure. Fail, and you will look at best inept and worse, risk being made the subject of ridicule, something you probably may not have encountered since school days but which believe me is something you have to beware of, even into adulthood.

One thing I have found quite interesting, if odd, in the course of putting together the films, has arisen when placing together a load of people notorious for butting in. Give them all a script, however, and get them to act it out...not one will interrupt and you begin to see amazing natural actors emerging out of them. It seems to be the case that if you are a person who butts in and talks a lot, there's a good chance you will make a very good actor/actress, or possibly be a very talented writer or composer. As you can see, there are many careers out there that I bet you haven't even considered - maybe it's time to jump out of your comfort zone and try something new? Try to remember though to avoid butting in, as no-one likes a person who interrupts too often, especially if they're talking sense!

17. Learn to Relax

This is something that a person with ADD ADHD can find really difficult to do! And yet at times we can be way too relaxed, to the point that we can hardly be bothered to move at all.

As you get older you will start to see a drive appearing, and this is the point where you start to think about doing your own thing a lot more. It can become a very powerful urge, and may happen at different ages, and it is a perfectly natural part of the growing-up process. A counterbalance must be found however, to avoid burning oneself out. The problem that people with ADD ADHD face is that they find one of their best ways of relaxation lies in work - essentially, they find that working is what can help to chill them out.

I have experienced this in the past, and it can put tremendous strain on family life - you must strike a balance between work and relaxation if you want to hold on to a stable marriage.

Music, exercise and sport are all very good ways of relaxing, but you need to work out which discipline is best for you. Obviously the hyperactivity in this condition is supposed to fade gradually as you move into adulthood, and the condition becomes more like ADID, or Attention Deficit Interest Disorder.

On a personal level I'm not sure about this, as I still experience many moments where my hyper moods can take over - actually I love it when this happens, as it's a time when I find I can work a lot harder and faster than normal. It can however become a problem when you are trying not to be hyperactive and all you want to do is relax. There are several forms of medication suitable for this as an adult, and your doctor will tell you about them. Valium is one that I have used in the past and I must admit that the results in my case were fantastic, but a major problem is that it can be very addictive, and for that reason I won't be taking this form of medication again. Quite frankly, if you want my 100%, totally honest opinion then I would say that the best form of medication to help people with ADHD relax is a natural plant called Marijuana (weed), but, unfortunately, its use is illegal in the UK. This is a very sad state of affairs, when an individual is forced to break the law in order to obtain the medication needed to help combat a medical condition, and this is something that I and others will continue to work on to get changed!

I have questioned over a hundred people with ADD ADHD if they had at any time smoked cannabis or weed, and of that figure over 90 per cent said that smoking definitely helped them to relax. The most beneficial thing is that whilst you are relaxing, you're not hyper or at risk of getting into trouble with the law. The only problem is, you have to break the law if you want to relax in this way!

It is however, quite possible to relax without any form of drugs at all, and this method has been around as long as humans themselves. Meditation is an ages-old, proven way of controlling your thoughts and bringing your body to a state of total relaxation, although it does take time to master and does require a little bit of time to do...though no more than building and smoking a joint I might add! Some of the thoughts that you have when meditating I have found quite amazing and I would recommend to always have a pen and paper close by when you are meditating as it can often produce moments of genius!

One thing I would like to emphasise here is that you are best trying all available natural methods of relaxation before resorting to drugs that you might become dependant on. The natural way is always the best way in my view, and I would stand by my research - smoking weed is by far the best available natural option. When the doctors wake up and realise this, it might hopefully be made legal for medicinal purposes.

There's always the added bonus that a stoned world would be a happier world!

The only way to help your child or teenager to relax with this condition is to keep them totally occupied and busy, admittedly not something that all adults can do. All I can say is, it does work for me though!

18. Alternative Therapy

This has begun to attract a lot more attention as people have become more aware of the nasty side-effects that can appear after taking some of the medicines prescribed for ADD ADHD.

There is now a vast list of herbal medicines and different ways to treat the condition but still I'm afraid it's a case of trial and error, in the sense that what works for one doesn't always work for another. There are plenty of specialists around who now claim they can treat these conditions without using highly controversial medicine. Though I have never spoken directly to any of these people, I have encountered at first hand families who say they have seen improvement after this kind of treatment.

Social skills therapy is certainly one that I feel is a massive help, and it doesn't matter whether you are a child or an adult, it certainly helps if you are part of a group that shares problems by talking to each other about them. There is also no doubt that stimulant treatment has proved itself effective, but you will first have to decide if you feel that young children taking stimulants from a very young age is advisable.

The only problem with talk groups and other similar treatments is that in the younger years children will struggle to both listen and engage in these kind of discussions, but it is still a very good place to meet people similar to you and ideas are often swopped around and sometimes people will find better solutions to their problems by attending these groups.

When it comes to adults I have no doubt that these groups are a massive help, and at worst you will find that you leave the classes with a lot more education on how to deal with this condition. I have a new favourite when it comes to this kind of treatment, very similar to the talk groups but without having to leave the house!

I have posted about 100 videos on the You Tube website which show all the stages that I went through in dealing with my ADHD. These have received well over 340,000 hits and they were also shown to pupils at a school for children with ADHD in England. Although many of the children and teenagers found the videos quite amusing, they were also full of facts and in my view you can't beat the reality of the first-hand account of an individual who has lived life with the condition.

What the school found was that the kids were able to focus and concentrate on what I was talking about because it took a more laid-back approach to imparting information about dealing with the condition. Once again I must remind you that there is no absolute cure, and the only way of getting around this is to learn how to deal with your condition in your own way!

One of the great pitfalls of ADD ADHD lies in attempting to hide away from a lot of the problems you encounter, and I have discovered first-hand that talking to people is a massive help which also encourages you to listen to people and this is equally as important. This is where talk groups are especially helpful and the videos have proved even more so, as people will happily sit and watch a video they find entertaining or interesting, particularly where it doesn't involve the often toe-curling anxiety of articulating painful personal experience directly to others. They can however at the same time relate to the problems that they hear on the video, as it is something meaningful that they have probably experienced in their own life, and as there's no way of interrupting a video, distraction ceases to be such a problem. Adults also get good results after watching videos, as they are likely to see many examples that probably would have helped them when they were younger. The good thing is you are never too old to start learning about your condition and when you take into account that there's a good chance your children will inherit the same condition, some of the things you learn as an adult can therefore be of great help to your own family.

I am no fan of taking medication to alleviate the signs of ADHD, but as we've seen, it is treatable with drugs. The receptors in the brain are the key to this, and I make no secret of the fact that I often smoke cannabis, or marijuana, to help combat my ADHD. These herbal drugs are legal in some countries but are illegal here and in lots more countries, which is a great shame as it is widely proven that they affect the receptors directly, and for me personally they really do help to calm me down and increase my concentration levels. Another option if you are reluctant to break the law is coffee, as it is commonly known that coffee can do the same thing as Ritalin, with the unarguable bonus of having practically no side-effects whatsoever.

Any kind of treatment for this condition is a very hit and miss affair, I'm afraid, and only time, and trial and error is the way to find what is most suitable for you!

I don't recommend that you give any of the drugs mentioned to children, incidentally, though there are people in America who are pressing for cannabis to be made legal in inhaler form, to treat all ages. I personally am unsure if I agree with this one though!

19. Islands

Here's a section I feel quite well-qualified in, as I have, as previously described, lived on the Isle of Man for most of my life, recently spending five months of each year living in Ibiza, another island...

I have researched my condition nearly every day since I discovered I had it, and have even lived alongside people with the condition in a deliberate effort to see how it affects them, and have found that for some reason the percentage of people with ADD ADHD seems to be very high in the Isle of Man and the percentage in Ibiza is a lot higher still! I have found a definite link between this condition and islands, and I genuinely think I could be the first person in the world to discover this. I accept that this may be the part where you think I have gone madder, but bear with me as I attempt to explain all. I call this "The TAPMAN'S Theorum", and the next chapter will take it to another level!

The percentage of people on islands with this condition is literally off the scale and although I am currently researching a lot of other islands to get more information, I feel it's better to use just first-hand evidence I have gathered personally as the main two examples in the book.

Smugglers in the old days as sea-farers obviously spent much of their time around islands, and with their gung-ho attitude and winner-takes-all mentality, displayed many of the outward signs of ADHD. Entrepreneurs, today's smugglers, operate with very similar tactics in business.

People with our condition just love this sense of adventure, especially where it involves an island, and this is more evidence to prove that explorers may have benefitted from ADHD. Another strong piece of evidence is the fact that people with ADD ADHD like to run away, to get away from all the problems they have created or that have been created for them by others, and what better place to run away to than an island? This is exactly what my father did when he was younger. If we consider that a lot people with this condition have ended up living on an island and then presume that this has been going on for hundreds of years, then it becomes easy to establish that people on islands can be very closely related. I'm not for a moment attempting to suggest that we are all inbreeds of some sort, but there is definitely a distinct "island mentality" between people, and some degree of interbreeding needn't be that far from the truth!

So then, if a high percentage of the people that already live there have ADD ADHD, the people who tend to come over to live temporarily are quite likely to have the same condition. Then if we take into account how hereditary these conditions are - basically 80% genetic across your whole family tree - it doesn't take a rocket scientist to see why the levels of ADHD are so high on islands.

I have concrete proof of this in the Isle of Man but can discern even clearer results in Ibiza! And as so often there is a very big positive to be drawn from all this. The people that you meet on these two islands are very special people and very different to the norm, in a very good way!

I am sat on the Manx ferry in the process of writing this section of the book and, after some time stuck on the Isle of Man due to bad weather, I'm actually excited about leaving on this next little adventure. Although I adore island life and wouldn't contemplate living any other way, I would admit they can get a little claustrophobic, especially if you get itchy feet as I do. Islands are amazing and I feel very lucky indeed to live on two of the best in the world - anyway, back to the evidence which backs up my crazy ideas!

IBIZA...has 5 massive nightclubs, holding in excess of 10,000 people and are open every night of the week for 4 months of the year... why why *why?*, because the people who built those nightclubs had ADHD and wanted to build the biggest and most celebrated nightclubs in the world!!

ISLE OF MAN...has the world famous TT race course, 38 miles long and which is basically a lap of the whole island - by far the biggest racecourse in the world!! Why why *why?*, because the person designing that race course had ADHD and wanted to build the longest, most dangerous track on the planet!

ISLE OF MAN...has the biggest waterwheel in the world - why why *why?* because the person that designed that waterwheel had ADHD and wanted to build the biggest waterwheel in the world!

There are many more examples that I could use here but I think there's ample evidence to prove without doubt that ADHD is linked to islands in a very big way. Statistics prove that the percentage of people with this condition is very high on islands and now I reckon we have a good explanation for "TAPMANS THEORUM"...ADHD is linked to islands, and it's up to the scientists to prove me wrong!!

If this section has raised your eyebrows, then keep reading, as what follows might well make you fall off your chair!

20. The Tapman's Theorem

What if humans did something similar to salmon and turtles and other animals and mammals that flock to the same place on the planet at a certain time of year? Everyone might think I've gone totally mad with this one, but could it be that humans could be attracted to special magnetic places on the planet, or more precisely a certain *type* of human being?

Es Vedra rock in Ibiza is the most magnetic point on the planet. Yes the North Pole strictly speaking is more magnetic, as too is the Bermuda triangle, but neither are accessible like Es Vedra!

I have often said ADHD is a gift and not a mental condition as we are led to believe! What if these types of people were drawn by some sort of magnetic pull to this one little island in particular? It may sound fanciful, but after spending so much time there, and meeting so many people with ADHD who have all said they just feel "drawn" to Ibiza, most of whom return year after year to the same little island, I feel less likely to doubt it!

It is known that the hippies, believers in ley lines, were drawn to Ibiza in the 60's by its magnetic pull, and I haven't met a hippie yet that doesn't have ADHD, I always said that if I had had hair (I was bald at 20), it would have been dreadlocks, and after spending four summers now with hippie types I am shocked how well I fit into their lifestyle.

Ibiza attracts the most talented entertainers, DJs and pop stars in the world, and I have got to meet lots of them, I can't remember the last time I met a 'normal' person there as talented as these people. And all from different countries as well I might add!

It has become a well-known fact these days that many of those who are really successful have got ADD ADHD or one of the related disorders which stand alongside.

At a certain time of the year hundreds of different species of animal set off on their migratory journey and go to a place on the planet where they nest, breed and feed, returning the following year to repeat the process. How do these animals find their way back to the same nests in the same places every single year? The answer is they use the world's compass and put their trust in the magnetic forces that have helped their ancestors find the same place before them.

This is a well-established fact that has been happening since animal life began on this planet - is it not possible that humans act in exactly the same way, especially a certain type of human? No surprise I'm talking about the ones with ADHD!

How can there be so many people with this condition on one island? Why do they travel to the same island, year in and year out, when the world is such a big place? Why do they all seem to congregate on islands all over the world? How many islands around the planet are renowned as party islands during the summer months?

Humans also love migrating, but as so many work or have full-time commitments, not as many get the opportunity to live the nomadic lifestyle that we all crave so much!

Ibiza is renowned for its fantastic nightlife and party atmosphere, the Isle of Man is renowned for its superfast car and bike racing and other motorsports, Ko Pang Yang is famous for its full moon parties, and a very different way of life! I could talk about islands forever and give you hundreds of examples but want to concentrate on one island, Ibiza, the most magnetic place easily accessible to man, the place that seems to have the highest rate of ADHD I have ever come across, anywhere in the world! A place people from all over flock to for the summer months and a place that is so full of talented and uninhibited people, it is literally the party capital of the world!

I'm convinced that there is something more which might explain all these facts and the more I look into it, the more I think that humans are also pulled by magnetic forces to different destinations!

I have named this "THE TAPMANS THEOREM" and if there's any scientists out there as nutty as me, then please look into it, for some reason I don't think the general public are likely to believe someone with a 'mental condition', unless his points are backed up by a professional!

Photography by chrisbevanphotography.co.uk

Photography by chrisbevanphotography.co.uk

Section 3

1. ADHD and Injuries

Would it be at all possible that people with ADD ADHD are more prone to hurting themselves than 'normals'? I'm afraid to break it to you that the answer to the above question is a resounding YES!

When you think about the above, you don't have to be some kind of Einstein to work out why. Try to think of someone you know who might have ADD ADHD and then try to remember how long you have known them and how many times have you seen them injured. You will be astonished how much this statistic stands out when you look at it this way, and again there are some quite obvious explanations why.

There are many examples that I can use here and I will start at the school playground. A plain old simple dare to climb the highest up the tree during the lunch hour. Who will be first? Who will climb highest? Who probably falls and breaks his arm? The person who has ADHD I fear! A combination of the thrill, the danger, the dare, the will to win and so on, and suddenly you have a broken arm out of the basic human desire to show off!

Additionally, and as I've said, I believe that a lot of top sports people also have ADHD and we all know how often they get injured, especially in extreme sports! These two examples spell out loud and clear that people with this condition will always suffer more injuries than 'normals', but there is also another way which is much more disconcerting.

People with ADD ADHD or the other related conditions are also known to self-harm and hurt themselves intentionally, and this is something that I personally have witnessed in the past. For some reason some people hear voices in their heads, and unfortunately these often encourage them to inflict pain or harm upon themselves. It is seen as a release, a cry for help, and is a major problem especially in teenagers. I have had conversations with several people who were self-harming, and am saddened to report that two of them are now dead. This proves a big point, that self-harming could well be the first steps taken before someone actually takes their own life. The condition is highly linked to suicide I am afraid, so be aware of anyone you might know who may be self-harming, and at least try to get them the help that they need - you might just save their life!

It's no surprise that if you have a massive will to win and you really do want to become somebody or attain something, you will be willing to take loads of risks to try and pull it off. When it comes to any kind of sport it stands out a mile that such risks will sometimes result in injury, and you won't find a great bike racer or Formula 1 driver who hasn't pushed everything a little too far and ended up sitting on the sidelines with an injury because of it!

This can be filtered down to normal everyday life as well. People with ADHD are always in a rush, especially when it comes to driving. I haven't looked at any statistics on this one but it's not really needed to be honest. People with this condition are known to drive faster than 'normals', always trying to jump the queue or beat the red light. This is caused by our lack of patience and our hate for waiting around in traffic, and in turn can cause more road traffic crashes than normal and of course such accidents will often end up with injuries. Does a person with ADHD get more injuries than normal people? Absolutely no doubt whatsoever!

I would never encourage anyone to go into any given situation half-heartedly, as this can have severe consequences, especially in motorsport! But, on the other hand I would encourage you to think just a little bit harder before you go head-on into any situation. You might well end up not just injuring yourself, but other innocent people as well, and that as they say is something that you might have to live with for the rest of your life!

You're always likely to take the odd gamble, but are the odds really worth the possible consequences? Only you can decide!

2. Don't Read Too Much Into Things

Whilst spending the last four summers in Ibiza living with people with the condition, different groups every couple of weeks, I have discovered lots of things about ADD ADHD and the way that people react to situations.

One of my biggest eye-openers whilst being around those individuals was the way that they react to minor situations and problems, sometimes making them into massive problems that don't actually exist! The best example I can use to demonstrate this came in Ibiza, when I went out along with a couple of well-known DJs to the biggest club in the world. We all had backstage passes to access all areas and found ourselves mixing with some of the biggest stars in the world! One of us had a discussion with one of the friends of a big star, who was so stuck up his own arse he made us all feel very uncomfortable. As the night went on, and after a few drinks, we all had a discussion and decided that we felt that we were unwelcome and that maybe we had upset one or more of these "important" people. Obviously we left soon after this and then spent the whole night talking, trying to work out why it had gone so badly and what we had done wrong, if anything.

People with ADD ADHD struggle to let things go until they have got to the bottom of situations, and none of us could leave this one alone! The next day, one of us went to another function to meet all the same people from the previous night to try and determine what the problem was, as we thought it might be better if we all didn't go together after what had occurred the previous night. We waited with anticipation for him to return, and after a few hours we got a phone call saying that everything was perfectly ok and there never had been a problem!

This was clearly a classic example of people with ADD ADHD reading too much into situations, where before you know it there are voices in your head giving you all the wrong signals! We had basically ruined our own night by all getting the wrong end of the stick and forced ourselves to leave as we felt so uncomfortable, yet all along we were more than welcome - in fact they were a bit annoyed that we had left!

This will often happen, even in trivial everyday occurrences, as we always tend to think the worst in situations that arise, we are always full of self-doubt and badly lacking in confidence, yet most of the time we are hardly the shyest people in the world!

The amount of times that I find I have to reassure musicians and DJs that their sets were brilliant is insane! No matter how well they have just played, they always have massive doubts about their performance. If the crowd isn't going totally wild then they feel that they have underachieved, not taking into account the variables, like what time of night their set was, or who was on after them. They just see negatives that don't exist and constantly cast themselves in a bad light, when invariably, it's not necessary or appropriate!

Children also often suffer from this lack of self-belief, and a good bit of advice here is to always reassure your children that they are doing a good job, just as the teachers should do at school.

There have been many times when I myself have got into such a state of self-doubt and fear, and looking back it was completely pointless and unproductive, but having ADHD, everything can feel exaggerated and you might find well yourself literally in tears. People cry usually when they receive bad news or are upset, but people with this condition cry much more easily than is usual, and in exaggerating this, you have the makings of a breakdown, it really is as simple as that.

This really highlights why it is so important not to read too much into things, and to keep a good firm control on your thoughts!

3. Everything Happens for a Reason

Try to learn and keep telling yourself that! When things are going your way everything seems normal, probably because in your head the outcome is already achieved.

This is a recurring problem for people with ADD ADHD and it is why we leave so many jobs unfinished. When things don't go as planned it can appear a huge catastrophe in our minds, even though the problem may not be very big at all. This can send us into a bit of a frenzy and plans as set out will end up not really of any use at all. This is the reason why I would advise you to plan as little as possible - obviously you have to plan all the basics in advance, but once you have a structure it's much better to let things go with the flow, this way you can allow things you haven't planned to happen, and they tend to happen much more organically, allowing you to react to them without beating yourself up over why this or that has occurred contrary to your original plans - and consequently, with a lot less stress to you.

Remember the phrase "everything happens for a reason", and another good one, "what will be, will be" and finally, "for every action there's a reaction". These three sentences alone might just be your answer to a slightly easier life at home and at work.

I really believe that it's true in life that you get back what you put in, things don't just fall into your lap unless you're very lucky indeed. One thing that I have learnt is that we have an amazing ability to turn a negative situation into a positive one, and this can only happen if you're in the right frame of mind. This really is another one of the secrets of this condition and you need to learn exactly how and when to use it to your best advantage. Sometimes you have to turn against your thoughts to break the routine that you might find yourself in, sometimes the urge will naturally take over and you will be treading new ground unconsciously. This has happened for a reason! The reason being that, for that one moment something inside you let go of normality, and you wanted to do what you wanted, instinctively and intuitively. This is ADHD!

You will instantly make the best of your bad situation with surprising ease, and your failed idea will have now been replaced with a bullet-proof goal, and success is just around the corner! AHA! If only it were THAT easy...

You will find that you can dig very deep and in many different situations, and as you solve a problem you will instantly look for another to fix, and so your determination will start to build...and all this is happening for a reason remember!... it's a force of will, just so you succeed!

Confidence is an essential weapon when you are battling your ADHD demons and with confidence comes positive thinking. Things definitely fall into place much more easily than forcing them into place and they tend to hang a lot better when fitted correctly!

4. Finding the Middle Ground

This is something that I have spent most of my life trying to find, and more often than not with very little success. When a person with ADHD works, they will either work at 100% or they will work at no more than 10%, in terms of efficiency. A more average individual might typically work at 33% most of the time, will live their lives at 33%, and will always have good organisation and usually money left each month to pay the bills, and maybe save a bit for a rainy day.

The "middle ground" is very obvious in a 'normal' person's life and I'm hoping that after reading this, a lot of people with this condition will be able to touch base with the middle ground far more easily than I managed at first.

"The Zone" can also be classed as middle ground, as it is a place where we are happy and content, a place where we can either totally focus or, on the other hand, totally relax!

My life can be incredibly hectic at times, and if you were to ask me when I last had a normal day, I probably wouldn't be able to answer. I love to work and play when I'm totally focused and completely in my "zone", and almost always then I function in the 100% area, I really struggle to do anything down at the 33% area - it literally tends to be all or nothing in my life! However, I wouldn't suggest this as an ideal. Instead, you may start off by spending as much time as you can in your "zone", but always leaving plenty of "middle ground" time, as you will find you can focus much more fully when functioning in the 100% area.

These days I try a different approach, "less haste more speed", similar to the tortoise and the hare scenario. I have found that if I drop back slightly from the 100% area I get more done in the long run, without making the mistakes that people with this condition so often make. The doctors will encourage you to take the drugs on offer and it is proven that they can help people with ADD ADHD find the middle ground platform, as long as you are prepared to cope with the nasty side-effects. This could well be the only option for young or extremely problematic children, but for teenagers and adults there are a lot more options. You do not need drugs as an adult to control ADHD! "The Zone" is the best place to be, and recently I've started meditating, which I must admit hadn't previously really been my thing - having said that, it is a good way of putting yourself more in the middle ground area, and a lot easier to get and keep yourself there.

This is one of those areas where you have to find what works for you individually-yes, the drugs help you with your concentration levels and this may be something that is very important during your final school years but it is not a decision that you will find easy to make, as there are both good points and drawbacks when taking medication for this condition. People with ADD ADHD can only function properly when they are happy and this is a really important point to look at.

It is very easy to see when an animal is not happy as the signs are there for all to see, especially if it's a pet, where you know all their habits off by heart already. However it's nowhere near as easy to spot when a human isn't happy, and especially ones with this condition, as they quite often bottle things up and hide from the truth. This can become a very dangerous time, and although you are always going to have "good days and bad days" you need to teach yourself how to keep a good balance. This means having many more good days than bad ones, where possible! The better the day you're having, the more work you will do, you'll find you cope with things much more easily - all in all, you will be operating in the "middle ground" area, and this is something that you will quite often have to find each day, because I've found that you don't always wake up in the middle ground area, not even if you were there when you went to sleep!

No matter how well you deal with ADHD, there's little doubt that you will have good days and bad days for the rest of your life, I'm afraid! Things that come naturally for 'normals' are more often than not something that we all have to strive hard to achieve: what a good thing, then, that there are so many advantages attached to our condition! Living and working as much as possible in the "middle ground" will always generally result in an easier time, and may be a lot more useful as a result.

5. I Can Hear Voices

One thing that is quite likely to form a big part of your life, whether you like it or not, is the odd voice in your head telling you what to do. You can take comfort from the fact that every now and again these little voices in your head are the secret to controlling your ADHD.

What makes a person who is standing on the top of a building decide if today is the day to jump or not? If there is a person there trying to talk them down, then that could have a good influence on stopping them jumping, but if they are on their own then the situation may be very different. All the person on the roof has is their own thoughts and their own voices, and from this they must make the choice of jumping or not. It's obviously a lot better when these voices are nice ones, telling you nice and positive things, and you can achieve some of the biggest things in your life by listening to these voices, but be aware that when you are in a bad place, these voices can control you in a negative way and send you completely down the wrong path. If you take into account how often we find ourselves in 'wrong places' with this condition, you might start to realise what a massive part these voices play in our lives!

I wouldn't dispute the fact that all people hear an inner voice in their heads to a degree, but I can guarantee you 100% they aren't subject to the number of voices in the head that a person with ADHD hears.

What should be understood is that these voices are controlled by our inner self and that is controlled by the place that you are in at that point in time! You have to learn to control the thoughts in your head, and more importantly you must remember which are the correct voices to listen to. This is critically important, as if you get it wrong, I fear the consequences could even prove fatal, if we recall the rooftop example.

I had a chat once with a close friend who told me that he had voices in his head telling him to harm himself. When you have such confusing voices as this, I think it's crucial to avoid taking wacky prescription drugs, and nor at all costs should you be drinking alcohol. I have seen way too many times the sorry effects which these can have on people and consequently on their families as well.

Another thing that comes from the voices in the head would you believe ie noises in the head, let me explain! People with ADD ADHD make noises with their mouths, nearly everyone I have met with this condition does a great Donald Duck impression. It's like a bit of a fidget but with your mouth and you probably didn't even notice that you did it until now! Human beat box is a classic example of how some people make a living from producing these noises. You have heard me talk about nearly every DJ I have met having ADHD, well there's one in particular who makes music way ahead of its time and the music he makes is built up from new noises and ones that have come from him making noises with his mouth, I would like to add that this guy is one of the best in the world! So it's not always voices in your head, sometimes it could well be noises that you hear and hence why we make so many daft noises with our mouths, and before you say "no I dont", I'm telling you that you do! This is another case of people with a suposed mental condition excelling at things that you wouldn't think, this condition still never ceases to amaze me and the more people with it that I get to meet, the more I realise that they all seem to have a lot of talent! I must add that all of the talent that these people seem to have is absolutely nothing that they have learnt at school! Still think the education system suits people with this condition? I think not!

Now I wouldn't want to come across as all Zen Buddhist here or anything, but - when we hear voices in the head, do they actually make a noise? Not one that other people can hear, obviously - though my dog can hear things I can't, does that mean *those* sounds don't exist, because I don't hear them? –no, I don't think so, either!

So, we must accept that the inner voice, which is real to me, is an electrical impulse which conveys a meaning that's particular to my brain, as no-one else will hear it - unless, that is, I use it to create a sound externally! I might bang a stick on a bin lid, or shout at the top of my voice, whichever method I use, you'll hear a noise for sure! This is where people with ADHD are at such an advantage when it comes to creating music. The kinaesthetic aspects of ADHD clearly helps them convert the electrical impulses they hear into an external form of sound - and like as not, they won't need reams of sheet music to follow!

Human beatbox is a perfect example of how some people make a living from producing such noises; it's an interesting phenomenon worth further study, but not here. However we have already established that nearly every DJ I have met has had ADHD, one in particular who makes music way ahead of its time and the music he makes is built up from an amalgam of new and found noises and ones that he makes with his mouth, and I would like to add at this point that this guy is widely recognised as one of the best in the world in his field!

6. I Wannabe Somebody!

We are constantly told, 'Everybody wants to be somebody!' But do they? I would contend, no they don't!

"Normals" for example are usually quite happy with their 9-5 existence and are more than happy to just be part of the consensus, as long as they have a holiday once a year!

Quite the opposite of a person with ADD ADHD, who is always striving to achieve more, never satisfied with their current circumstance and always wanting more! If nearly all people with this condition are always wanting the great success and wanting to become 'somebody', why is it the percentage that actually succeeds is so very small? What happens to the rest? Well the answer is a lot more straightforward than you would think!

When someone says they want to 'be somebody', it doesn't necessarily follow that they want to be a famous rock star or film star, some may have other ideas.

When you look at the section on "jobs for ADHD" you will see a vast range of different things that suit all of us individually. When someone wants to 'be somebody', they might well want to become a police officer, or a firefighter or just a plain old artist! One thing is certain, most will achieve at what they set out to, but what happens to the 'failures'?

Such a label can really pose big problems for people with ADHD who, it should be remembered, have already very likely encountered the label throughout their school life. Further stigmatisation at a later stage can quite frequently lead to depression and sometimes suicide. Failed business, failed marriages and being unable to hold on to a job - there are always people who set out to 'be somebody', to achieve a goal, and who 'fail'! But we live, and fail, by our own standards - not by someone else's.

The big difference that stands out with people with ADD ADHD is that when they say they want to be somebody or achieve, they mean it and seem to have extra reserves they can use to make their dreams happen. Don't get me wrong, this is not down to a mental or physical difference to 'normals' and people with this condition are no better or worse than 'normals' in any way, but they definitely have an ability to dig that little bit deeper and push themselves that little bit further. Perhaps this determination is the result of the experiences felt during their schooldays.

A perfect example of this determination is a world champion cyclist from the Isle of Man. From a very young age all he wanted to be was a professional cyclist, and he is now current world champion and has won over twenty stages in the Tour de France in the last four years. His dedication is amazing and he totally lives, dreams, eats and sleeps cycling.

When you go into a gym as a world-class athlete, you will hook yourself up to heart monitors and all available modern technology to see where and how your body can improve and in turn make your performance improve. He is intrinsically no different to the rest of the world-class sprinters! He doesn't out-perform them, his body doesn't perform any better than his opponents, and technically he shouldn't be any better than his competitors on the track. During an interview I watched on television I heard him say how he has this ability to dig very deep when it comes to the crunch, and this is where he finds the extra speed to leave his competitors in his wake. To stand out this much in the world of cycling or sport in general is clearly not very easy, as they all have similar bikes, kit, training methods and so on, so how can this one man turn the screw so much in the final stages of a race enabling him to make the best in the world look like they are standing still, even though on paper he is no better than the rest?

The answer is simple - ADHD. I firmly believe most top elite sports people have the condition or one of its relatives and without it wouldn't be able to do what they do in the final stages of their chosen competition!

When you have this "I must win" attitude, and as long as your body is performing exactly as it should, your ADHD is equal to an extra gear, another secret weapon in the box, and when you focus on a certain thing, there isn't much likely to stop you achieving your goals!

Without this commitment there is no way you will ever be the somebody you so desire to be, but if you are blessed with this massive will to succeed, the chances are that one day you will end up being that somebody, the secret being never to give up! Something that people with our condition very rarely do!

7. I'm Bored of Talking about Me ...Let's Talk about Me!

I have already talked about the problem we face with butting in during other peoples' conversations, and another huge tell-tale sign of this condition is people talking about themselves a lot.

My excuse is that I've got a lot to talk about, but to 'normals', this tendency can cause some resentment, and half of the time you won't even realise that you are doing it!

I have had to train myself over the years not to talk about myself all the time, yet I still find this hard, especially when you take into account that most of my conversations currently involve people asking questions about myself or the film. I always make sure that I take time to ask other people things and do my best to keep the conversation revolving around others and not myself. Unless of course I'm doing a prep talk or something similar, then you'll have to listen to me!

Another reason suggests itself why others with ADD ADHD are given to talk so frequently about themselves. If their average day is anything like mine, I'm sure it will be packed with lots of dramas, even when just trying to have a normal day! Obviously this promotes the things that happen into worthy stories and of course you just have to tell them to someone!

I have got some of my best stories filed away in my brain, all itching to get out and be told, but I tell myself there's lots of time and one great story every few meetings is plenty, no need to overload people with loads of useless information about yourself! If your stories are truly good enough, then there will come a point where people will pay money to hear them!

Okay, by then you will likely have even more stories, but the point I wish to make is still the same. Let other people speak and try to bounce some of the conversation around, so you don't end up always talking about yourself. Trust me when I say that, the less people hear, the more they will want to hear!

Another fault that really stands out, especially in children, is that they will butt in simply to talk rubbish, basically take the conversation off on a totally different tangent. Why do they do this?

Maybe it's because the current conversation is too detailed for them and they have no pertinent information to add to the current topic, or maybe it's just the plain and simple fact that the conversation is boring them to death and they feel it needs a change in direction. Either way it can become very annoying, very quickly and will almost certainly antagonise everyone involved. Situations like this can remain in people's minds for years and years, so it is highly advisable to stop yourself doing this as soon as you can.

If you have a family member or friend who is interrupting constantly, then I would strongly advise you to talk to them about it and reach an agreement that you will stop them if they go too far. This might be very difficult to do at the time and might well cause an argument, but they will thank you for it in the long run - even if they will never admit it!

I have got all the meetings about getting the film into the cinema over the next four weeks, and after all this waiting I am literally itching to get talking. I know that to get the best deal for the film I will also have to do a lot of listening, and I'm also going to have to keep it buttoned as and when some of these people slag the film to bits, which they probably will do. I might feel that it's perfect, but if they are investing a lot of cash in advertising the film I'm sure there will be changes they want to make.

This is definitely a time when I will need to listen politely without letting them walk all over me. It's going to be a very important conversation and one in which I must be careful not to butt in, unless of course it's absolutely essential. I know that every time I interrupt during the conversation the chances are I will lower my chances of signing the film. Maybe this is one of those times when I would be better wearing a gag, but I've been training myself to behave during this meeting, as it's so obviously such a big part of the whole project, and I feel sure I can adapt. This is definitely an area that you will find you too will be working on forever, but like anything to do with this condition, it's all fixable, one way or another!

Consciously remember to always let others be involved in conversation, it will make your life much easier in the long run and maybe a lot more interesting as well. It's not always all about you, and you must respect the opinion of others, unless they are talking complete nonsense, of course. Then, it's open house!

8. I'm Not Living in Denial..am I?

Of course you're not! And neither am I!

This is one of the biggest faults of the person with ADD ADHD, and the funny thing is that hardly any of you will even know you're doing it. Like most problems arising from this condition, you can only fix it when you know it's broken.

Only after my film director Hambi sat me down and talked through this with me, giving me direct examples of how I live in denial, did I even realise quite how big an issue this is.

I must admit, I was totally shocked when he explained certain things to me and it was only when these were pointed out that I even realised I was guilty of them - but at least now I know about it and can make a priority of fixing these faults, individually minor but collectively, massive!

A glaring example of denial is the alcoholic, drug addict or even shopping addict - you ask any one of these if they actually have a problem and I guarantee that none of them will say yes!

ADHD means we usually have a very addictive personality, and are particularly vulnerable when it comes to various forms of addiction. Having the willpower to stop drinking, smoking etc, is only half the battle and until you have accepted that you have a problem there is no way on earth that you can begin to deal with it!

So stop living in denial because if you don't, it might just be too late to fix what you have gradually broken and as we know only too well, even then, these kinds of thing are not fixed overnight! I have sat in a few talk groups made up of people with ADHD or similar conditions and just getting someone to one of these groups is a big achievement in itself, as it's often the first time that an individual is actually admitting to a problem and wants to beat it.

Whether it be drugs, alcohol or mental issues, these groups are very often successful and can be key to someone making a full recovery from one of their demons. I think it's only after seeing or being involved in something like this do you realise that you have yourself been living in denial, and as I said earlier, it's only when you admit to this that you can begin to fix the problem that up until now didn't exist!

As has been said before in this book and will be said again, 50% of a cure lies in accepting a problem, and to do that, you have to triumph over the perfectly understandable human tendency to deny the unpalatable, even to yourself!

Stop living in denial and you will find that your life changes for the better. Quite often we are scared of the outcome of something that we have done, or even worse, of something we may have become. If you have an ailment, just a simple trip to the doctors can become one of those massive challenges that require a huge effort for those with ADHD to complete, but which more often than not once accomplished, result in you being in a better frame of mind, as you now know what's wrong with you. This is all about ceasing to live in denial - there might well be something you find difficult to accept, but remember that where there's something wrong, there's a better chance that it can be fixed, if only you let them fix it!

Sort yourself out in this way and you find these problems will certainly diminish, and might even vanish altogether.

9. Itchy Feet - The Traveller

It's from our daydreams that many people with ADD ADHD get a lot of our ideas and this is one of the reasons why we are often so keen to get out on our travels. Whether it's because you have just had enough where you are and need a change, or maybe you are running away from something or possibly chasing a dream, you will find that this condition does make you want to get up and away quite appreciably more than 'normals'.

I am very lucky to have holidayed and raced rally cars in many different countries, so I feel like I've already seen a lot of the world, but in the last five years my itchy feet have returned. If I was to be totally honest, I'm more at home living out of the back of a van or under the stars in Ibiza way more than in the comfort of my lovely house in the Isle of Man, maybe it's just the hippy in me.

People with ADD ADHD just love moving around, and for some reason many of them seem to end up settling on islands (see the relevant section on islands) - how strange is that?

People with this condition will probably go through at least part of their lives living a bit like tumbleweed, it's as if we all find ourselves whilst living like this. No major routine to worry about, no bills to pay, no-one to answer to, no television, basically you can do what you want, when you want to...

The only folks I know who haven't lived a bit of their lives in this way are the ones that are dying to! I have met hundreds of hippies from all over the world in the last few years and nearly all of them had ADHD. Each a total individual, unique to themselves and famous for being drawn by magnetic force to the island of Ibiza, the true home of the hippy.

The reason hippies live the way that they do is because they don't want to be part of the modern society and they thrive on having the freedom to move around, they are among the soundest people I've ever met in the whole world, they have such a laid-back attitude, never appear to have many problems.

How different would the world be if everyone lived like this? One thing I would say is that it would be a damned sight friendlier!

The hippies have got it just right, and so too have the travellers...this condition makes you want to move around, avoiding the boredom of a static existence and helping cure those itchy feet that keep annoying you so much!

Let yourself go - you will know when the time is right - break the mould, and do something you wouldn't normally do, something that you have only dreamed about before...this is what makes dreams become reality, let your natural person shine through a bit more and you might be pleasantly surprised in what you see! Book the holiday you have talked about, or buy that camper van and go see Europe! ...stop thinking about it, and just do it! You never know when it could be too late, and you will beat yourself up forever if you don't at least have a go, what can go wrong? ...and ultimately it doesn't matter anyway if it does go wrong, as you can always fix it.

Remember that if you are one of the entrepreneur-style people with this condition you might well get to see some of the world through your work, but because of your addiction to working you won't have as many normal holidays as you might like, so may need to leave the work behind: don't tell the wife just yet though!

10. Less Haste...More Speed

Another one of my mum and dad's favourite sayings and yet again, another that is totally true to life, especially if you have ADD ADHD.

We have all heard the story of the tortoise and the hare and we all know who wins the race in the end, but does this mean that if we slow ourselves down we actually work faster? When I work, I work at 100% - nothing more and nothing less - but when analysing a project after it is completed we can always see areas where we may have done better. Maybe if we were to attack each project a little slower and plan it more carefully we would not only save time, but would also probably save money, the number one rule in business.

People with this condition have the ability to work very fast but spend a lot of time fluffing around and making small errors. I'm so looking forward to making the second Ibiza film for example, because I can identify so many places I could improve on the first.

As in everyday life where sometimes you have to go backwards to actually go forwards, this also applies to addictions where you need to take your life back to the bone and then start to rebuild yourself by replacing the addiction with something new. The same system should be applied to your everyday life. Instead of rushing into decisions and getting stuck-in straight away, why not try to take a bit more time in your planning with the consequence that when you come to execute your plans you will find that everything runs a lot smoother.

How many times have you rushed around making a cup of tea and in the mad panic just as you are about to pick up the cup, disaster, and you spill it all over the worksurface instead? A classic scenario of "less haste more speed": if you had slowed everything down a touch, you wouldn't be faced with having to make a new cup, or worse still, not having a cup at all.

Another phrase that I would like to incorporate into this section is "a little bit at a time". When faced with a project or real-life situation that requires a lot of time, energy and focus, the whole picture can be enough to make someone with ADD ADHD not want to start it at all!

It might well be their own individual project, or it could even be painting the lounge, but the thought of how much effort will be involved can easily overload your brain and make it a struggle for you to find the motivation to carry out the task. The best advice I can give you in this situation is to try a new approach, and just do it a little bit at a time until you get into the groove, just like the 'less haste, more speed' dictum, in a way.

How do you think someone like me can sit here writing a book, when by my own admission I can't even sit still for more than 10 minutes at a time? Trying to discipline myself to write everyday has proved a massive test for me, bearing in mind I've read only a handful of books in the last 30 years: it just ain't my thing, so to speak! The way I get round this is very simple indeed! I will write two sections of the book each day, no more, no less, and although this is a definite commitment, I do allow myself the whole day to complete this. I find that in this way - more haste, less speed - my brain stays in the zone once I have persuaded myself finally to begin. When I wrote the film script it was a totally different method, I sent my wife off to see her mum for a couple of weeks, and turning on the hyperfocus button, wrote the whole thing from start to finish, only stopping for food and sleep when I was tired. I must admit this totally drained my whole body, and wouldn't recommend this approach unless you are on a deadline as I was. Obviously when I read back what I had written there were many mistakes, and this backs up the heading of this part of the book "less haste...more speed", one reason I've adopted a different method here. Even when you feel on fire, and in the element of your zone, try slowing back a little, and the difference in your results may be incredible!

11. Monks...What do They Know?

I am not a religious person, so won't be trying to force any kind of religion down your throats, and if there's a fault in the American books on ADHD it comes, in my view, when they start rambling on about religious things, which does my head in to be honest, so the only, slightly religious section in my book will be about monks and what they say.

I was going to list all sorts of links in this section to YouTube videos that different monks have posted, but they are very personal at times and although I would strongly urge you to watch them, you will have to hunt them down yourself, which may make things a bit more interesting for you (plus I can't be bothered finding them for you) - only joking!, one of the best is called something like "everything will be alright"? While the videos are not specifically directed at people with ADHD, they do nothing if not talk sense on how to deal with a variety of situations in life, are both informative and very relaxing for people to watch and listen to, and before you laugh, give it a go, I think you may be pleasantly surprised!

When I was down and in a bad place a friend sent me one of these links, and after sitting and watching a monk talking to a camera for 45 minutes I felt in a much better place and my title I think says it all: "Monks..what do they know?" - well the answer is absolutely loads that will help you at your worst, so you have got nothing to lose by having a look!

I'm not suggesting anyone run off and join a monastery, and I'm certainly not encouraging a vow of silence (how could I?) or walking around bobbing your heads devotedly, but these guys are in a good place and don't very often talk, so when they do I would suggest it's worth a listen! In all seriousness I can't stress to you enough how much these videos have helped me, especially when I've been experiencing a down day. Everything they say means something, and they speak directly from the heart. You won't hear rubbish coming out of these guys' mouths. Don't be going picking a fight with them either! They are some of the hardest people on the planet and they don't take no shit! They study all forms of self-defence and martial arts. In fact, the only negative thing I can find to say about monks is they don't get out enough, ha!

That and - they're very intelligent people who talk total sense, if only everyone was like that! Enough said!

12. Music is the Answer

Whether it be playing an instrument, singing, writing music, DJing or just listening, people with ADD ADHD just love music! I have been quite heavily involved in the music industry for a number of years now and can see that a high percentage of people who are really into music have ADHD, and the really talented ones, those who stand out a little bit more than the rest, all seem to have the condition a little bit more intensely than others.

Almost the whole of the entertainment industry is made up of people with ADHD and a massive percentage of the music industry is the exactly the same!

Music can be used to help us in so many different ways: driving is much more pleasant when music is playing for example, and believe it or not a lot of people play music whilst doing their homework, or some other intensive task. There aren't many things as good as listening to your favourite songs whilst relaxing on the couch or in the sun, and how many people go jogging or to the gym with an I-pod these days? The answer is nearly everyone, it's as though music has become everyone's best friend, we use music to comfort us and we also use music to prepare for things. Top sportsmen and women nearly all use music in some way to help them train and more importantly, to get in the "Zone" before a big event! Music can also be very calming, and this is something that really helps people with ADD ADHD, especially after a flip out! Music can help to bring us out of the bad places we find ourselves in, and can inspire us to achieve great things. It also comes in very handy at work. How many times do you see a painter and decorator working without music, even a local radio station? Not very often!

I have recently had a couple of weeks off from writing, as it had become, for the moment, counter-productive. In all honesty the daily routine had become something of a grind. Now though, the trouble I'm having getting back into it is a nightmare. Today is the first day I have written more than one chapter since my break, and I think I know the reason why.

I am sat listening to the just-completed soundtrack to the film, and although I recognise all the tunes from the editing stage, this is the first time I've actually had an opportunity to sit and listen to them in full. This seems to have put me in a perfect comfort zone to write merrily away - this is now my sixth chapter today. All the words are flowing, and I hardly have to think as I write, so smoothly is it all flowing onto the computer screen as I sit here listening to amazing music. What a terrific example of just how much music can change both your mood and your mind, putting you into a zone where you can function to your full potential.

Would I have achieved this so easily without the music playing? Absolutely not. In fact I'm virtually bounding around the room, and it's not just because of the music, either. The thoughts I'm having, knowing that I am making such good progress with a project that had seemed to be moving very slowly has given me a massive inspirational boost, and I can see me just wading into this every day from now until it is finished. This is ADHD at its finest! The hyperfocus button is set and we have the ability to push ourself to get the job done!

If things aren't going your way and you feel like everything is getting you down, just turn up the music! The results will amaze you, every time!

Music is a great thing for not only putting you in a good place, but also putting your emotions in the right place, and one thing I will guarantee is that when you're emotionally sound, life with this condition becomes a hell of a lot easier.

Relaxing to music is one of the best therapies known to mankind, and there's nothing better in my view than relaxing to soft chilling music. So treat yourself to some Ibiza chillout tunes or some smooth jazz, and you can just melt away from everybody!

13. My Good Friend, William to Win

Obviously, Will to Win is related to my other friend, Will Power (see next section), and it's hard to believe how differently we react when referring to will power and the will to win.

A person with ADD ADHD can have the greatest will to win you are ever likely to see in the human race (as long as they are firing on all cylinders), yet the same person's willpower can be dreadfully low, all depending on what the situation is.

It's all very well having the most amazing will to win, but you have to be very careful, as this determination and commitment can be the undoing of a lot of things around you, without you even noticing it. Many people race away with a dream or an idea and will stop at nothing to achieve this, the trouble being that, when all is well and everything is achieved, you find that many of the things you had around you are gone.

The will to win in elite sportsmen and woman is probably the most important ingredient in becoming a big success or to be outstanding in your field. Some people have this will to win to such an extent that it drives them to explore a lot of the possibilities which might enable them to win, which may include cheating by taking performance-enhancing drugs or, on the other side of the spectrum, ridiculous training schedules and very strict diets. Without the will to win, sportspeople would literally get nowhere.

This obviously transfers over into business, as the will to win becomes something more like the will to succeed and in bad circumstances, the will to survive. From a small, one-man concern right up to the large industrial giant - none of them will succeed without someone in charge with a huge will to win. Winning in business comes when you can manage to turn a profit, not so much through competitions as such, although if you do really well there's a good chance you will win awards. I won young entrepreneur of the year, and I can say that there's a great satisfaction to be had from winning awards in business as you instantly know that you are making a profit!

Obviously business has the same pitfalls as sport, and you will often see the will to win take over when it comes to making money! Just like the cheats in sport, so there are plenty in the world of business. People who copy products, sabotage opponents, fiddle taxes, flout the authorities and launder money are in abundance all around the world, these are just like the Olympic cheats in my book, nothing but scum!

One thing I've learnt is that there's nothing better than an honest buck! And obtaining money through cheating just doesn't seem the same! Don't let your massive will to win convert you to the dark side!

ADHD will make you want to break rules, make you want to cheat - anything you can do to succeed, survive, earn money or even just win that game of Monopoly! This is the time when willpower is more important than your will to win, and one reason why so many people with this condition end up in jail on fraud charges! They think they can cheat the system, and more importantly always think they are going to get away with it, never thinking they might get caught, but as we all know, in this day and age, they often will!

Jail isn't meant as a nice option, it also happens to be much worse for people with ADHD, the thought of not being able to come and go as we please, the constant answering to people, the restriction and having to behave are all things that go against the way our mind is set up. Stick to rules and let the natural will to win that you have been blessed with do the work, don't let your ADHD take over and bring the naughty side out of you - it just isn't worth it! It's a long road back to success once you have fallen from grace, and I really hope you take the above advice on board, because I am very well-qualified to comment on this area of the book!

14. My Good Friend, William Power

The close relative of William to Win, in the previous section of the book. Shortened to willpower, you might now grasp exactly what I'm talking about and how the lack of willpower can be the biggest downfall of people with ADD ADHD, especially when it comes to impulsiveness and addictions.

Without lots of willpower any person with this condition is vulnerable to some of the very worst things in life, especially if we are talking about something that the person in question has been addicted to.

People with ADD ADHD do suffer more from narcotic problems than 'normals', this is proven in research and it all starts at the simple point where someone is looking for a bigger buzz! This is why people take drugs at first, simply to get a buzz! But how often do we hear of people getting addicted to drugs and their life spiralling out of control? As we live in denial, you will never realise that you are addicted right up until the point where you find the willpower to stop or to say no! It's only usually afterwards, when people are clean from drugs, that they will actually admit that they were dependent on them. This is a shame, as if we had just had the strength of character to admit this earlier, we could have gathered more momentum from an earlier point and the willpower would be a lot stronger, possibly resulting in us being able to conquer our demons much sooner, allowing us return to normal, everyday life.

Willpower does not surround just substance abuse, by the way. Without it we wouldn't be able to grind out results from all sorts of other situations, and to make them into positive ones! A negative result where willpower is involved can result in tasks not being completed and situations overpowering us which, again may end up with the negative consequences!

Positive thinking plays a massive part here, and you will often see sports people psyching themselves up before an event and talking out loud. This is their way of getting in the zone, building themselves up and increasing their willpower for the task ahead.

When faced with a situation that appears to have you totally beaten - even though people with ADD ADHD simply refuse to be beaten - you can find yourself very down and out. Only by digging deep into your willpower and will to win will such situations become retrievable, to complete the task in hand not only with ease usually, but also in superfast time.

Just like your "hyperfocus button", willpower is one of the most important things for a person with ADD ADHD. I have had the most horrible day today for example, with alterations to the trailer for the film, and getting feedback off people. My way of cheering myself up has been to leave a funny Facebook status but just writing what I put made me want to go out and do it. I said something like I felt like going on a bender, but my good friend William Power kept telling me not to! After pondering the idea for a few minutes, I added to the status that the bender can wait for Boxing Day in two weeks, but I must admit that for a few seconds I was very weak and was very close to actually succumbing to temptation right there and then!

How often in the past have you done something like that just on impulse? Quite regularly I imagine… learn to let your willpower take over the bad voices inside your head, even to speak back to them sometimes. When you hear "let's go a bender" in your head, answer to that voice, "no thank you, I'm busy" or maybe something a bit more charismatic, ha ha! - there's nothing wrong with having an argument with yourself if it stops you doing something you shouldn't! You have heard the phrase, "have a word with yourself" –well, that's exactly what willpower is for, and you need to learn when to implement it.

Although it probably sounds like I'm having a bit of joke, I can assure you I'm quite serious as, believe me, having a word with yourself is what may possibly one day save your life!

15. My Way or The High Way

I have gradually come to write different sections of this book dependent on my mood, or what kind of day I've had. Today has been crap by the way! But, I have just watched the final edit of my film, "Ibiza - My Way or the High Way" and I just can't think of a better time to write this particular part.

You should all know by now that this book isn't like most books connected to a film, but is more about the condition ADHD and how to deal with it. What I haven't told you is that you will hear many of the titles from this book mentioned in the film.

I didn't want to ramble on about ADHD too much in the film, so decided to include it instead by lots of sayings and actions that you will see both in this book and in the film. Basically these should all make sense when you see the film or read the book, depending on which you do first. Either way you will now have to do both, and that's clever business! What did I say about ADHD and entrepreneurs?

HERE IS A QUOTE FROM THE FILM:

"Ibiza, the white isle

I came here to build my dream

A brand, famous not just on this isle

But all around the world

Now you might think that's a tall order for an ex-rally champ

from the Isle Of Man.

But people like me....with ADHD

Always reach for the stars

SCOTT BRADSHAW...IBIZA MY WAY OR THE HIGHWAY

I even named the film based on this condition-it's my way or the highway, you either listen to me, or you're off! This is a person with ADD ADHD in a nutshell, and the title of certain chapters in the book quite often appear in the film. Anyone who has ADHD will totally relate to this film in everyway, and they will find it highly amusing. I'm hoping people will also see what this condition can do to you, good and bad, and after watching it they will look on the condition in a totally different way.

I wanted to make the book as interesting as possible chiefly because people with this condition usually don't like reading - it's much easier to sit and watch a film, but how often do we then read the book connected to that film? Well, I've never done it, and to make sure that a lot of people who watch my film will read the book as well, I've combined it with a full spectrum on the condition, hoping that there's a little something for everyone in it!

Making this film has been full of ups and downs, just like the life of a person with ADHD, and throughout the book are many real-life examples of how to try and deal with these things.

Unfortunately for me I think that by no fault of my own I have just landed in a situation which is about to become a big problem; let's see how I deal with it!

I have just travelled all day from the Isle of Man to Liverpool to watch the film and list final amendments so that I can start trying to market it. Please bear in mind that the boat was already a day late and I was also very excited to see how much the film has progressed! After going the wrong way on the motorway for 10 miles I eventually arrived at Hambi the director's house, all perky and ready to start. We sit down to watch the film and instantly it fails and needs rendering, he shows me how to do it and I proceed following the instructions. The first very tiny piece I do, it flashes up 35 minutes, bear in mind this was only five minutes of the nearly two hours long film!

My whole body starts to boil, and I can feel ADHD starting to take over. Words can't describe how angry I am and, then it gets a whole lot worse!

After 20 minutes of rendering, it decides to crash, saying 'memory full', and I can't do anything about it until Hambi returns in two hours. My head is very close to going. This would be a tough situation even for a 'normal' to handle, but to anyone with ADD ADHD this small problem is growing into a major catastrophe...so how do I deal with it? I know nothing at all about editing software, and I can feel myself getting more and more angry. *This is now taking place exactly as I'm typing it*. I keep getting urges to scream like fuck, but there's a girl next door so I can't, I feel like smashing the computers up and if I was in my house, that's probably what I'd do! I know that the day is now a total waste and the reason for my visit is put a good foot up the arse and I need to get things back on track.

I've just been outside for a fag, it's bloody freezing, so I'm gradually getting more and more pissed off, I really don't feel like I'm handling this very well at all. This is the kind of situation that makes so many of us slip up!

I'm now going out to the car, to get myself into my zone and probably smoke a joint...for the first time in ages, I am having to pull out all of the stops just to keep on a level playing field, the car, the zone and the weed all in one go...lets see if I can come back in a better frame of mind...........

15 minutes later

What has just happened is one of the worst ADHD moments I have had for at least a year and I'm now sat here with a different attitude. There's no point in rushing around, as I can't fix it. There's no point ringing anyone, no point in getting angry, no point in shouting at anyone - even though I really feel like it.

The way I have dealt with this instance is to apply the tried-and-tested "fuck it" attitude - it's not a life and death situation, it can be fixed eventually and after my little tantrum to myself, everything seems to be a lot better... Everything happens for a reason, what will be, will be!

PS...I'm still very pissed off, but as each minute passes, it all gets a bit easier! This is a class example I think of my condition getting me into a muddle and making me nearly lose the plot, to no effect. As you take on bigger things, there is a good chance you will see situations like this a lot, and you have to learn how your brain reacts to these instances and instantly work on fixing the impulses. Even now I am still struggling, as you too now know!

Nobody wants to be involved with someone who looks like they are out of their depth, or even out of control, so dig deep and you can overpower most of these scenarios, just be prepared for the one that pushes you a little too far, they can creep up on you at anytime and before you know it, you're full of regret again.

16. Reach for the Stars

This is another of those classic sayings that I think sums a person up with ADHD and it's one that I use in the film!

If you have a dream, then there's absolutely no reason why you can't live it, I'm a firm believer that anything is possible if your mind remains totally focussed on that subject until completion!

You'll notice I use the word "completion" - how many times have you set out on a big mission and not long before completing it you find yourself already on another one?

In the past this has been one of my biggest downfalls and when both book and film are completed, they will be the first big projects I've ever managed to finish in my life, not because I'm lazy and can't be bothered, but more because I tend to just jump straight into another project and so on.

This is something that you have to address before you will achieve any form of decent success, even in everyday family life you must learn how to finish things. It is without doubt one of the biggest nightmares for people with ADD ADHD.

The way that I look at dreams and ambitions is a bit like a Walter Mitty-type might I suppose but why can't anything be possible? The barriers exist in your head - just because something hasn't been done before doesn't mean it's not possible, in fact many people with ADD ADHD permanently strive to do things that no one has done before. Whether in business or mad challenges, like Sir Richard Branson's space - and balloon-rides for example! He has all the money in the world and still risks his life on breaking world records to achieve the impossible!

On paper, what I'm in the middle of doing is totally impossible! Make a film, write a book and produce a soundtrack in the space of fourteen months? Who in their right mind would attempt something like this, especially when taking into account that all three areas are totally new to me. I wanted to set myself the biggest challenge that I could think of and wanted to make it especially hard for myself in the process. Why?

The answer is simple! I have got ADHD and I want to be the best at everything I do in life, especially if it can be achieved without destroying the lives of everyone around me, a crucial balance you have to strike! It's all very well having the drive and ambition to pull off the impossible, but must take great care not let it damage your family life in the process, this will be the key to succeeding with all your dreams. Remember, if you feel you must reach out for something that is pretty much out of reach, first make sure you have the people around you to hold onto, who will keep an eye on you! When you are left to tackle things like this on your own it can quite easily be your big downfall!

It could be that you need a trainer to get you in shape if it's a sport you're trying to excel in, or it could be that you need a secretary to pick up all the paperwork that you leave unfinished in your new business venture. Either way, you have to have people around you if you are going to succeed, and without a good team around you there's a good chance you will fail. I know this from experience and although I have done all of the work to write this book, I'm still sending it to a good friend to go through it and put it into words that are easy to read and spelt correctly! Similarly, when making the film I wrote all the script, but did send it to a writer to double check it, and then after filming had a professional edit it all and make it really *look like* a film. My point is, you can't do everything on your own, especially if it's something that you know very little about. If so, you will fail!

I have as much determination as anyone, but feel I'm realistic enough to accept that there are certain things that you need help on, and only when you acknowledge this will you be able to reach your ultimate goals.

When someone is successful it is most often because they and the people around them have created some form of a movement. I can't think of many people who have done it literally all on their own. So, set out your goals, research everything in great detail, and then put the people around you in place to make it all happen-if you do all this, then there's a slim chance you might just pull it off. You only get back in life what you put in, it's a fact! Don't expect things to happen just because you have a good idea, it just isn't that simple, long hours and maximum effort are also major parts of the equation, and this why you will always need support.

Don't let anyone tell you that your dreams are impossible, as that will very likely just make you want to prove them wrong, and the gung-ho approach which results can often lead to failure. My advice on this subject is based on my past failures and current successes, but if you really do want to pull off something that shouldn't really be possible, you will need 100% commitment, a little luck and good people around you, and maybe then you can "reach for the stars" and live your dream as I am doing now. If I can do it, anyone can! It's as simple as that.

17. The Drama Queen

How many times has someone told you to calm down, to chill out - how many times have you been called the drama queen?

If you are anything like me this section heading will have played a massive part in your life, and personally, looking back I see there are so many things that I could have done differently.

Reading too much into situations definitely makes people with ADD ADHD react in many different ways to any given circumstance, quite often blowing the trivial situation totally out of the water and making a big scene - hence the term "the drama queen".

However, this can also apply to something constructive, believe it or not. Why are there so many people with ADD ADHD in the music and entertainment industry? Well this is the easiest answer in the book...because they all play the perfect drama queen. From what I have seen in recent years, people with ADHD seem to make fantastic actors, to a point at which 95% of the cast in my recent film have got the condition! In fact I casted the film before actually scripting it - totally the wrong way to do things apparently...or is it? I wanted to try something totally new that no-one had ever done, so I picked some huge characters who I knew had ADHD and built the script around those, knowing intuitively that they would all make terrific actors. None of them had any kind of training incidentally, but the results I think are amazing. I find I have to keep reminding myself I have just made a feature film and not one person in the film was a professional actor, but nearly all the people in the cast and the crew had ADHD! The result is a totally true story involving actual people in real life, all of whom have a supposed mental condition! This is a perfect result as the performances are amazing, as I hope you will agree when you watch the film! Trying to execute the whole thing in a different way to anything anyone has done before, pushing rules and boundaries in an effort to stand out from the crowd - something us folk with ADHD are among the best in the world at!

This demonstrates that sometimes being a drama queen isn't quite such a bad thing after all, especially in the entertainment industry! But back in reality you will find you must learn to deal better with certain situations, as none of us like to be labelled a drama queen, especially when we know it's a much more complex issue than that - so don't give people the ammunition! Learn instead to deal with sticky situations, and don't make a mountain out of a molehill!

If you feel yourself getting all dramatised up, take a step back, get yourself into your zone and deal with it swiftly and calmly. This is another example of how people with this condition often read too much into things and blow situations completely out of proportion, quite often making a minor problem that should be easily fixed into a massive one that seems impossible to fix. We have seen how we don't react well when faced with a major problem, yet possess an ability to turn bad situations into successful outcomes by the power of positive thought. If a problem is small and can be sorted out easily in a calm and collected way, you will find that the "drama queen" won't even need to put in an appearance! Like in many situations involving the condition, prevention is better than cure and you really need to work on preventing these bigger situations from occurring, as at the end of the day many of them are expanded simply by your thoughts, so effectively can be controlled. No need for any drama! Unless of course you decide to become an actor, and then you should find that you have plenty of it already built into your system.

No-one takes to a drama queen, especially in the work place, and as we've seen, individuals with ADHD generally have problems holding onto jobs for any long periods of time, so this is something that you really do need to address!

Section 4

1. Do Not Pass Go!
Do Not Collect £200!!

As we've established earlier, I like to write this book according to the kind of day that I've just had, so why write a section on jail when, as today, I have had such a good day? Simple - I have just read an article in the local paper, and the headline read, "MAN SMASHES UP LOCAL PUB". Now while I have nothing in particular against my local hostelries or the leisure trade in general - though I have some doubts about that - as I read on, I see that the man in question is one of my close friends. Why is this important? Well that man has recently been diagnosed with ADD ADHD at the age of 38! Although he has spent time in jail before, it was many years ago and he had stayed out of trouble for a long time.

Luckily this time he was given a suspended sentence, but it strikes me as a great example of how the temper associated with this condition needs to be tamed - and usually the only way that can happen is by learning how to deal with the condition yourself. Learn to avoid, or if not swiftly remove yourself from, situations in which you're at risk of a flipout! Alcohol is nearly always a factor in such situations and as always there will be a lot of remorse virtually instantly when the deed has been done.

A temporary flipout can be easily avoided by not drinking so much or by taking yourself out of that situation and putting yourself into your zone! You will find that after a few minutes away from a confrontational situation you will deal with it totally differently. These often small situations can escalate very quickly, and before you know it you can be in the back of a police van, next stop court and possibly jail! I don't have an official figure on the percentage of people in prison who have ADD ADHD but imagine it's very, very high!

I had a very short spell in prison sixteen years ago, and looking back it was probably the best thing that ever happened to me - that is, apart from the fact that it cost me my rallying career and any prospect I might have had of getting a proper job ever again! This is a real and continuing problem, because after just one trip to jail you will struggle forever to get a decent job, quite often resulting in repeat offending, and then you are on the criminal path for a good proportion of your life. The often-quoted expression, "he's done his time" simply doesn't apply here in my experience, though it may make some people feel better, fleetingly.

Reflecting back on my own time in jail and sticking to my theory that ADD ADHD breeds talent, I am absolutely convinced that this is true! There will always be an amazing artist there, a terrific guitarist, a great comedian to keep everyone laughing and always great sportsmen…the trouble is, none of these people have learnt how to control their condition and in the end it's the condition that controls them, and ends up sending them back and forth to prison for many years to come.

Maybe they should start educating inmates on ADD ADHD as it might just help people learn how to deal with the condition, and as it is connected to other similar conditions I don't see that it can do any harm to those, either.

Some of the writing that comes from inmates is of remarkable quality, and worthy of the professional. John McVicar was one such prison inmate who famously went on to make a career from writing and was the subject of a major feature film. I believe many could follow along similar lines, but who will employ an inmate to write parts for famous actors to play? Obviously I would but, I'm afraid to say I am very much the exception!

In my opinion everyone deserves a second chance, and as there is so much natural talent sat there locked up it seems more than a shame for none of their work to ever see the light of day and get recognised. Prisons should encourage art and writing amongst the inmates, because you can't get stories half as real as the ones you hear in jail! Obviously if we could channel these talents and utilise them before they get banished to jail it would be so much the better, there really is no need for some of the prison population to be sat stewing in jail, learning how to become a real villain, they just needed educating on any condition they may have, and on how to cope with it from a younger age! They should be being identified at school and educated in a slightly different way. The results would be miles different, and benefit everyone!

2. Say what you Think…or Should I?

If you're anything like me, you will struggle not to say something especially if it's troubling you.

We always tell ourselves that we are right, when quite often we are actually wrong. Speaking out about certain things can very easily offend others, and we all badly need to learn to filter what comes out of our mouths at times.

I have fallen out with a lot of good friends in the past because of things that I have said - sometimes it's better to keep your thoughts to yourself, and I admit I'm still struggling on this one!

This is a totally different issue to the "verbal diaorrhea" identified in an earlier section of the book, and is probably much more serious, as I see a clear link to a condition like Tourette's syndrome. It is now medically confirmed that Tourette's is linked to ADHD and similar conditions, and I found this out first hand and in the most embarrassing way when I accidentally said the F-word live on a radio show in the Isle of Man. I didn't mean to do it, and have never done anything like this before, something in my head just couldn't stop me from saying it. I'm no different to many other people with ADHD-and Tourette's - in the sense that I swear quite a lot, usually out of frustration and this becomes something of a habit, I'm afraid to say.

I met a guy in the summer who suffered from ADHD very badly as a child and he was telling me how one day at school, in his head he began to see the teacher as an old, wrinkly skeleton which should have been buried years ago! Guess what came out of his mouth? Yes indeed, the very same thought translated into words and sure enough, another detention and trip to the headmaster's office, and another symptom of this disorder to look out for!

Tourette's can - though not necessarily - be even worse. I'm sure you have seen at least one of the several TV programs on this syndrome, where people can out of the blue shout rude or offensive words, seemingly without regard to the consequences. They may often just shout whatever they are thinking…if they see an overweight person, for example, the chances are they will shout something along the lines of, "you fat bastard", sometimes even placing their hand over their mouth immediately afterwards, in disgust at what they have said. They regret it instantly but for some strange reason just can't stop themselves from saying it.

The TV programs on this subject may come across as very funny, but you don't need to look into this syndrome too deeply before realising it really is something very nasty and which can totally ruin a person's quality of life.

There are similarities to all this in ADHD, and this may be why we are so opinionated and so keen to get in our tuppence-worth when we feel it is required. You have to learn to control what comes out of your mouth, because you really can do yourself a lot of damage socially by saying the wrong things at the wrong times!

Think before you speak and after a while of not landing yourself in hot water or making a fool out of yourself, you will find that this becomes quite natural and you don't even have to think twice before you speak. This will only happen however after you have landed yourself in tricky situations with your mouth on a few more occasions!

Remember once again, this is only fixable by you, and no-one else can help you fix this ever - recurring problem!

3. Live Your Dream

When I told my parents of my plans to make a film, they just laughed and called it a pipe dream, good job I never told them that the real dream was that I'd use the film to launch the building of a global brand!

I will briefly explain my dream right from the start up to where it is at the time of writing this book, and you should see that, no matter how big your dream is, anything is possible when you put your mind to it!

My basic dream was to build a brand as big as super-club Cream in less than five years without the huge investment normally needed to pull it off! Here was the plan - go to Ibiza with a brand and get our faces on a TV show that was being filmed there in 2008 - which we actually managed to achieve! The TV show was screened on the UK Living channel, and was the perfect platform to launch our fledgling brand, with over a million viewers watching each show. The next year would be a massive step, as I decided that we needed to make a name for the brand by hosting boat parties, and after a very long and hard summer we were rewarded with the prize of third best boat party, something which I was really proud of.

The time had now come to learn how to promote club nights, albeit on a smaller scale than Ibiza. I decided that a winter of TAP nights in the Isle of Man represented the best option, and after six really successful nights I felt like I knew everything!

The following summer came the massive test of trying to take the brand to the next level in Ibiza by getting my foot on the ladder of promoting - if you can make it in Ibiza, you have basically made it in this industry and the world is then your oyster. This was much harder than I had expected, but by the end of the season, and with a mixture of parties under my belt, I felt like the time was right to announce the film. The idea of the film was to tell the true story of a man called the TAPMAN (yes, it's me!) and how he built a brand in Ibiza and then made a film about it, and the film was also going to raise awareness on the condition called ADHD. If I could manage to get it to cinemas then all the people who watched it could attend massive TAP nights in one of the biggest clubs in the world and then my dream would be nearly complete. On the back of the film would be TAP management, TAP the record label, TAP productions etc, and once all this was in place I would have achieved my original dream of building a famous global brand in less than five years.

At this moment, I'm about one more year from success: the film is made and will be completed in two weeks, the soundtrack is nearly finished, and will be released when the film has opened, on the TAP label, and finally I'm off to Ibiza in a fortnight for meetings with the biggest club in the world about massive TAP nights there this coming summer, one small problem! I still haven't got the cinema deal, so what do I do?

I take the gamble and plan the big TAP nights even without the cinema deal. I know there's no way we can fill the club with over 10,000 people. On the other hand, if the film goes to cinema, we have every chance of filling the club weekly all summer. What's needed here is a big pair of *cojones* and a lot of bravery, but I've made this whole dream come to life by achieving each bit in stages - a little bit at a time! - and have to look at this as just another stage. Once this bit is accomplished I will have not only lived the dream, but also made a film about living that dream and now I'm nearly there the ADHD has taken over and nothing will stop me finishing this, and I even have the sequel planned!

Like I've always said, "anything is possible if you put your mind to it" and as you can see after reading this, no dream is too big!

What I didn't tell you before is that I discovered I had ADHD one year into the above five-year plan, which explained everything to be honest! People with ADHD often set themselves quite ridiculous challenges that can sometimes take over their lives, even to the point where the dream can actually take their life. Do not bite off more than you can chew, as failure can quite often be just too devastating to cope with! Like everything to do with this condition it may be a bit of a gamble, but if anyone is best equipped to live the dream, then it's a person with ADD ADHD - as I intend to prove!

Who knows - I might even be able to squeeze a book on ADHD into the plan somewhere?

My next five-year plan is to make five brilliant films whilst consolidating TAP as a world famous brand and hey, you don't even want to know my 10-year plan!

Always go for your dreams, you only get one life, one shot, don't spend your whole life regretting what you didn't do!!

4. The Business...the Boss

Remember the statistic? The alarmingly high one that said most of us don't even make the fulltime workforce? Where do we end up then?

People with ADD ADHD have a big problem with authority and are not very good at taking direction from people, especially if they think they know a better way of doing that job. We have an amazing gift of being able to think totally outside of the box, sometimes called lateral thinking. We are good at finding the best solution and are very quick-thinking so we are probably very employable in the wider scheme of things! The trouble is, we tend to want to be our own boss and a lot of us will end up being exactly that, or team leaders or similar. You will find that you will go through several different trades over your working years, as we get bored of doing the same thing and are always looking for new things to get stuck into. Don't be afraid to change! You will know yourself when you find something that suits you, how long it will suit you for only you can decide.

It isn't all roses being your own boss by the way! But some good advice is that you only get back what you put in, so if you do manage to create your own business, make sure you put the hours in, at least for the first couple of years! Take into account the large failure rate of small businesses, and don't go into business if what you are doing is your hobby. I tried this years ago and I don't know anyone who has made a big success from it, keep your business for business and your hobbies for your amusement.

Quite a lot of you will start out on your own from a very young age, already knowing in your heads that you can't work for anyone else, and your natural instinct is to get stuck in and try new things. For others, it's a totally different process, it may take many years of working for other people and getting ordered about before one day, unexpectedly something inside you will rebel. You may have experienced this already in your teens and in your later school years, but might have accidently drifted into the 'normal world' in order to bring you security for the future. This is, and never was, a place that you can fit in in any way that is totally comfortable to you! Eventually you will start to get urges, asking yourself if this is what you really want.

A lot of people get to thirty-five to forty before realising that there's more to life than doing a nine-to-five job, but their reasons for waking up to this can be many and varied. One man, or woman, could go through life working very hard and then just decide out of the blue that because the mortgage is paid and the kids are growing up, now's a good time to start a small business doing something that they have always been interested in. On the other hand, it's also common for someone to work for a company for many years and one day there will be a disagreement at work and this is the day that they say, "sod this,

I'm setting up on my own". The guy already has all the knowledge he needs, can get the investment by remortgaging the house, and can probably steal half of his boss's clients in the process. Two very different ends of the spectrum, if both totally understandable in their own way, and at the end of the day ...yep, it's night again! Ha!

But, if you have a condition like ADHD you have to accept that one day there's a very good chance you will end up being your own boss. We make successful business people for all the reasons outlined, and statistics prove that nearly all the people with sufficient initiative to start their own business or who have the capability of running a large business have this condition.

Don't be one of those that spend their whole life thinking about what they could have done, for God's sake! Life is too short and you are only here once - no matter what religion you believe in, you won't get another crack at this!

I have spent three of the last six years messing around trying to decide what to do when if I had decided earlier, I could have spent those three years channelling all of my energies into my latest venture, achieving more in three years than in the last fifteen!

Hindsight is a wonderful thing, but until you break out of the mould and take a bit of a gamble you just might never find out what you were capable of! You can always just get another job if it all fails...but remember you have ADHD and failure is not an option! Start to use your secret weapon and quite literally see how far you could travel!

5. Light Bulb Moments

Light bulb moments are basically a quick flash of genius or sometimes insanity which take over your present state of mind, they are spontaneous and you never know when they are going to come! They usually happen when you are daydreaming and can quite often happen when you are sleeping, but trying to remember them afterwards is a problem!

It's a fact that you only use a very small percentage of your brain when you are in a conscious state; most of your best thoughts come when you are either sleeping, or in a sleepy state, so if you can access these thoughts, surely they are the best things that are going round your head. I can literally jump clean out of bed from a sleeping state if I have an idea that's good enough.

I remember one day whilst filming in Ibiza in summer 2011, I jumped out of bed and ran up to the rooftop so I didn't wake anyone up with all my shouting and screaming after having a massive light bulb moment and coming up with a really good idea. These instances might not happen to everyone in this way, but similar ideas can spring from nowhere when in a daydreaming state.

They are more frequent when sleeping or semi-conscious, but very rarely do we remember them! Even when you have a pen and paper next to your bed, it is very difficult to just wake up and write something down, especially as it takes us so long to get to sleep sometimes, but this is something that you simply must discipline yourselves to do!

How many times have you woken from a dream and then drifted back off to sleep, only to remember nothing the next day? It is very frustrating, to say the least, but one of your special talents if you have ADHD is the ability to have the most amazing dreams, and if you can develop the skill of remembering them you are in for a real treat! You would be amazed how many people in this world do actually get to live their dreams, dreams created by light bulb moments, when you are in sleep mode, and they are dreams that one day could actually come true!

Everyone experiences light bulb moments but some definitely get a lot more than others. My brain never seems to stop working and sometimes it seems I'll drive myself and those around me crazy, but I couldn't imagine the day when the light bulb moments stop coming. I can honestly say that I have translated about half of these thoughts into real-life projects and this is where we can be at our most creative. If the idea is a good one you can sometimes dream away and even visualise it in your head working perfectly. The dream doesn't only create the ideas but can give you a good inclination of whether or not they are likely to be successful.

If you are blessed with an ability to dream up new and daring scenarios, ideas or tasks then you are equally blessed to pull some of them off. Start to believe in yourself and even the dreams can maybe become a reality. Every idea has to start somewhere, and trust me when I say...they all start off as a little dream somewhere, in someone's head! Hence the saying "that's what dreams are made of".

One way that you can remember moments from your dream state, whether it be daydreaming or even full sleep mode, is to try and write them down. I actually keep a pen and pad by my bed at all times these days and the second I awake I try to write down the last thing that I remember, and find in that way, as the day goes on you can actually start to remember other parts of your dream.

These dream moments are obviously a lot easier to remember if the idea has come to you whilst daydreaming, but I would still recommend writing them down! Quite often the minute you have a "light bulb moment" the thoughts can be erased from the brain as quickly as they came.

6. Del Boy Deals

On the way to becoming a successful entrepreneur, you will come across many Del Boy deals, and if you're anything like me there will be plenty more. I struggle to turn down the chance of a "good deal" and this is why I have struggled to hold onto full-time employment and have always ended up working for myself.

If you have a bit of a Del Boy personality I can assure you that your best option in life is to work for yourself, whether it be starting off market trading or ebay, this could be you taking your first step to starting up your own thing! People with ADD ADHD more often than not either end up in high leadership jobs or alternatively, working for themselves, rather than taking orders from others.

No matter how rich or poor you end up, this is one instinct that will never leave you, and the buzz from earning money or equally as good, the buzz of finding a bargain or steal is one of the best in life!

As an example of this tendency, I reluctantly had to take our massive TV to the amenity site today, though the very thought of giving things away goes against the grain, especially when it works perfectly. Anyway, whilst I was there I saw a 70s style white and blue swivel leather chair, and within seconds it was in the back of the car and on the way home with one very chuffed new owner!

People with ADD ADHD seem to have an incredible instinct for business and this is the reason why this condition breeds entrepreneurs with such regularity. There isn't a person on the planet who doesn't love earning money as it creates for most a massive buzz inside, and this is the reason we gamble so much, just in case we win big this time. In the real world we always lose more than we win and when you eventually realise this you will probably find your life entering a new phase!

As these entrepreneurs grow, so does the scope of their business deals, but they never lose their original instincts and if they can buy something for a pound and sell it for two, then they will be delighted to do just that! I have great memories from school of earning money in the break times either by playing cards, toss the coin and even selling sweets - anything to give me that buzz of earning money.

I suppose it's no surprise then to hear that when my son Maxx was five years old I was called up to his headmistress' office because he had been selling his lunch and sweeties to other pupils. What really surprised me here was that he had no sense of the true worth of money then - yet he still ended up with a pocket full of money each day!

These little things are defining in how you will end up in later life, and if you have this kind of instinct from a very young age there's a very good chance you will have ADD ADHD, fact!

Market traders are a classic example of people with ADHD. How many times have you met a market trader who didn't have the gift of the gab? Well, at least the ones that have been doing it years. The adventure of taking a risk and buying something knowing that you have to sell it for a profit is still without doubt one of the great feelings in life, but not to the same degree for 'normals'.

Stockbrokers virtually all have ADD ADHD and are quite often burnt out after only ten years in the business because the stress levels are so high in buying and selling large amounts of shares. I see this still to this day as the ultimate "Del Boy deal" and something which when I have sufficient money I intend to enjoy getting stuck into! The ultimate gamble, the ultimate risk and if you get it right, the ultimate reward - cool hard cash in the hand, and that buzz that we so often search for. Remember that this time next year we could be millionaires! Always go with your Del Boy instinct - it's another gift that comes along with that supposed mental condition called ADHD.

7. The Extreme Human

In the book "The DaVinci Method" the author Garret LoPorto refers to people with ADD ADHD as "DaVincis" and often calls them "The Total Human". This just about sums it up - almost perfectly - but it doesn't include the madness that so many of us indulge in, and for this reason I would rather refer to us as "The Extreme Human": always the risk taker, always pushing the boundaries of life, and more often than not taking things to extreme levels!

Please do not be offended by the title, as my only aim is to sum up a person with ADHD succinctly, and mean it to be taken more as a compliment that you are being referred to as the total human, while as for the extreme human…well, I imagine you already knew that!

How many of you reading this have tried your hand at some kind of extreme adventure? Nearly all of you I'll bet! We thrive on excitement and the thrill that extreme situations give us, 'normal' things bore us to death and quite often so do 'normal' people!

It's not all good news being an extreme human by the way! We usually leave a massive trail of destruction behind us and quite often it's our friends and family who are left to pick up the pieces. We are also a nightmare to live with and as I have said before, we go through 2.6 marriages on average. This could be one of the reasons why so many people with this condition actually end up together, along with the fact that no one else would put up with us. My wife deserves a medal for putting up with me, I'm forever leaving cupboards open, losing keys and a lot more of the daft basic things that torment us all our lives.

Even our marriages are of the extreme type, quite often fiery and usually highly sexual - not too surprising when you put two people of a similar breed together!

One area I believe that we excel in by comparison to 'normals' is the way in which, in the really extreme situations, we can usually pull something very special out of the bag. I have used top athletes as an example previously in this book but it doesn't always come down to sport to see examples of this.

In business some of the really successful entrepreneurs work for 18 hours a day, always on the hunt for the next big thing. I used to go home for tea, then return to work till 2am and then go home for four or five hours' kip before starting the process again. There isn't a normal person on the planet that would work to this kind of schedule on a regular basis, and I firmly believe that without this condition, none of us would be able to work to the extreme like we do! Just like the top athlete, we seem to be able to dig deep and just plough into these situations as if they are the norm. I don't think the body of a 'normal' would be capable of sustaining this day in, day out, and I know that I have made my body used to it. I can easily survive on four hours sleep a night for a week, it's as if it's second nature. Remember if you're pushing yourself to these extreme measures you must be an extreme human, or as Mr LoPorto calls it, "the total human". Either way, this is definitely one of the huge advantages of having ADD ADHD, and one you should learn to use, especially if you are thinking of entering the world of business or trying to get to the top of your sport. You really are built like an extreme human, and you will be very pleasantly surprised to see how far you can push yourself when you really have to!

Just remember you're not invincible, and you can fail and hurt just like anyone, you are not Superman!! Even if you think you are!

8. Scattered Minds

This has to be one of the best ways of describing a person with ADD ADHD and it really is down to you and you alone to master the curse of the scatter brain! Constantly changing your mind about things, always drifting from one thing to another and more often than not walking around in some sort of daydream. Nothing happens for people with this condition when you are in scatter mode, you will probably find that you get less done, and sometimes even end up going backwards on things.

We always leave things to the last minute and then get ourselves in a right muddle, which is simply solved with a little more time and maybe now and again a little preparation, something else that we struggle with.

One thing that you will have to get your head around is the fact that we are and always will be, slightly different to everyone else and if you're anything like me, you will have known this from a very young age!

You can learn to deal with so many aspects of this condition and when you take into account that there is no cure and never will be, dealing with it is the only option you have! This isn't something that doctors can teach you, the only way to do this is by reading books and researching on the internet - just remember to read the good ones!

If it's scatty people trying to give you advice on life skills then there's a good chance that not all of those pieces of advice will work for you! I'd like to think that I've been honest all the way through this, and although some of my examples may sound a bit extreme, then that's because they are! My life has been full of extreme situations and I have spent a large proportion of it asking myself the same old questions - why am I so scatty, why does my mind always wander off onto other things? Well I'm afraid that's just the way that we are built!

Having a scattered mind doesn't mean that you will have a scattered life, but it is going to take mistakes and mishaps for you to realise where you will have to make your own individual changes. Change is a good thing, and you should be getting used to it by now, as you have spent most of your lives being indecisive and changing your mind all the time.

You will always find yourself getting bored, and this will haunt you forever, you will definitely find that the times when you are bored in older life are those when your mind will start working overtime, and you can literally send yourself scatty!

Always try to keep your scattered mind occupied, and always try and keep one step ahead of boredom otherwise you might find yourself driving yourself mad...which is easily done, by the way! Your mind works in strange ways and you will find that you suffer from mild mood problems at best. Bi - Polar disorder is a much - exaggerated version of this, and if your temper or moods are off the scale maybe you should be reading up on this related condition.

Your mind is very individual and because of this each case of ADHD is highly individualised and unique to each of us, which could be why it can be so hard to detect and why so many highly-qualified people have misdiagnosed the condition for years and will continue to do so until they learn more about it.

Diagnosis should be split between patient and doctor as he won't be able to do much unless he knows exactly how your mind works, which isn't easy, to say the least.

You would think that if you have a scattered mind, then routine would be an essential, but this couldn't be further from the truth, as routine is not good for people with this condition. You will find better results by planning as little as possible and by trying to let things go with the flow a bit more.

Don't try and cope alone! You are always going to need someone you can talk to - this may seem very obvious but try putting it into practice, as you will be pleased with the results!

Your brain is always going to be this way. Adjust your daily routines and work to find the best balance for you - but be warned, it's all rather a question of trial and error.

9. You Thinking What I'm Thinking?

We have all heard the story that some identical twins can actually communicate with each other when they are not together. I believe this is totally possible and before you think I've gone mad, no I'm not saying that people with ADD ADHD have the powers to do this!

What I am saying, and this again is from personal experience, is that I have witnessed many occasions when certain people that I have been with could actually read what I was thinking right up to the point where they would tell me not to say something before I had even come out with it.

I have also noticed that with certain people I have the same kind of ability, which can be a massive plus, especially if you are trying to suss people out in business.

Yannis has many times stopped me from saying things I may later regret, and it literally feels as if he can totally read my mind at times, and if you were to ask him he would say that he can indeed read my mind. I know I have the ability to get inside people's heads and usually have a very good idea what they are thinking, even before they actually say anything! This is another one of those weird talents that once mastered, you will be able to use to your advantage all the way through your lives. It also comes in very handy when you are working closely with someone on a project. A good example of this is when you are filming, if everyone has an idea of how each other works you will find that communication can be achieved without so many words, which I admit is not exactly mind-reading, but it's not far off and certainly another great weapon to have in the armoury. Hopefully sometime before the end of this book you will all start to see a different side to this condition and realise that it does have some really good plus sides to it.

Obviously the better you get to know people, the better you understand them and this normally takes a lot of time, and the more complicated the person, the harder it seems to get to know them, and the longer the process will take.

Here is one for yas! How many times have you met someone and got talking to them, not even necessarily for a long time, but you just seem to click with them? How many times have you said the words, 'I feel like I've known you for ages'. My feelings are that ADHD people are extremely good judges of character and even after talking to someone for just a short period of time are very capable of deciding whether these people are the kind of people that they enjoy talking to. This is highlighted when talking to a 'normal' person, when you will usually find their conversation is boring and uninteresting and you will find that you drift off and are soon talking to someone much more interesting. I find some people totally fascinate me, especially if they are a bit different, and it's usually these people that also have ADHD, backing up my theory that these types are definitely attracted to each other. As we have usually lived our lives a little different to the 'normal' types of people this is probably why we struggle to relate to their conversation and we often feel that we have nothing in common with them.

You will know straight away when you connect with people and you will also know virtually straight away if you will be able to work around these people or even play with them. These are the ones where you will feel after only a short space of time like you have known them for years and you will find also that these are the kind of people that will more than likely be able to read your mind, and every now and again one will appear who is equally as good at it as you are. These are the people you should be spending your time with, as these are the ones that will help teach you more about yourself!

10. Playboys…The Big Kid

The only thing that changes as men grown up is the size of toys that they have. People with ADHD quite often think they are a lot younger than their actual years and this shows not only in their behaviour but is also quite obvious in the size of their toys collection, and I ain't talking model trains!

The bigger the kid, the bigger the toy - I am referring to toys like jet skis, quad bikes and speed boats! I was at a house this summer and every toy I've ever dreamed about was there - a Harley in the living room, jet bikes, Jeeps, and all sorts of extreme gadgets! The guy who owned the house had ADHD, a massive list of dreams and I could see he was just ticking them all off as he found he could afford them. What gives him the drive to want all of the finer things in life, is it the hunger for success, the constant need to earn money or the spending of it even faster? - his ADHD, I'd say.

You will struggle to find a man or woman who doesn't like blasting round on jet skis or cruising around on a Harley Davidson, but for most people in the world this is something that might happen only on holiday when you treat yourself or if you are lucky enough to bump into someone who will lend you one. There's nothing wrong with wanting fantasy-style toys in your life on a full-time basis but you do have to be prepared to work very hard to achieve this, not only are they expensive to buy, but they are also very expensive to run!

The main problem that I can see in others and feel in myself is that if you work hard and do earn a lot of money the urge to spend it and splash out on unnecessary toys is massive!

I have earned plenty of money in the past and looking back there's so much of it that I just wasted on buying daft toys - this is something that you would do well to learn to control.

I remember when I first had a little bit of money after selling a business I went straight out and bought a 32-foot power boat and whole host of inflatable toys to try and injure myself whilst being towed behind it, and the next thing I bought was a jet ski. Before I knew it I was having the most amazing fun, living one of my little dreams that I had longed for forever but was still totally skint and could hardly afford to eat, as I had spent all of the money so fast. In my head I could just go out and work hard and earn it all again, and although this is the best attitude to have, life doesn't work like that and you could put the same effort into the same project at a later date, but there's a chance it won't be as successful as previously. You have to remember that no matter how good your initial way of earning money was, there's every chance someone has done it, and cheaper, in the time that you have been absent and pretending you're a playboy!

I'm glad to say that I have now set myself a limit and when I do eventually have some money to spend again, will spend it more wisely, and instead of dreaming of being a playboy I'd rather work harder and enjoy being a playboy whilst on holiday like everyone else...Well, I have an eye on the new KTM racing quad, and when the time is right, I will be treating myself!

Remember the section in the book on injuries earlier on? Well another little tip for all you wannabe playboys...do you know how many rich and famous people get seriously injured or killed when are playing on all their expensive toys? The figures are staggering, and I have witnessed first hand on many occasions people getting badly hurt playing around on toys at parties, especially people getting drunk and showing off, always wanting to be the centre of attention - another one you have heard before in this book!

Remember to control your instincts, sometimes it's not big and it's not clever to raise off up the road on a quad bike at a BBQ! The power of the toys is a hard one to resist with a condition like ADHD but you have got to be careful - I'm not saying don't do it, as I'm always the first on the toys myself, but remember how dangerous it can be! Your injury might not hurt so much at the time, but believe me it hurts for weeks afterwards!

Only as recently as when filming Ibiza: My Way Or The HighWay this summer I experienced the above first hand. One of the actors in the film got offered a ride on his friend's bike, and sure enough he fell off, missing two weeks of filming. At least he lived to tell the tale, but there are plenty who don't!

11. When you Gonna get a Proper Job?

This is another one of my mum and dad's favourite sayings, but if I'm honest it is one of my pet hate sayings. I've already mentioned the percentage of people with this condition that have problems holding onto a 'proper job' or even stay in the workforce at all!

As much as you think you can train someone to be an artist the fact is that they are gifted with the talent first, then they learn how to do it properly. For these kind of people, the chances are they will end up being an artist as a living, and this represents a good example of what a 'proper job' entails. An artist may spend two days painting a picture and sell it for £400 pounds, which is obviously £200 per day, the problem being they will usually only work a few days a week. Don't ask me why this is so but it definitely is the case and this can also be seen in other careers that suit ADD ADHD. Actors/actresses quite often have this condition and they will work for one month solid, long days and well into the evening but when between jobs can go for weeks doing nothing at all! This is why you have to pick your career very carefully indeed and, when you take into account that a normal nine to five job is quite often not suitable for those with this condition, you might have to look slightly out of the box, something we all seem to do naturally by the way. Please don't think I'm suggesting that if you have ADD ADHD you will never hold onto a full time job, plenty of people do! Just remember that it probably won't be a normal nine-to-five! People with this condition generally go for jobs in the civil service (the police and law are also common) and most of these jobs involve strange working patterns, something that ADD ADHD individuals actually seem to enjoy more.

Be careful what you determine to be a proper job, as more often than not with this condition it will just not suit you! Here is a list of my jobs through my life and you will spot some very weird ones! First I worked in a bank, then drove funeral cars, became a car mechanic, a car salesman, professional rally driver, rally instuctor, exhaust fabricator...After these I decided to go it alone, and ended up being the boss of a car-sales garage, a tyre garage, three clothes shops, an extreme sports shop and a website, and also had a large ebay shop on the side!

You will find more help on choosing your career in the "jobs for ADHD" section of the book.

At the age of 40 I decided everything needed to change as I was bored of all of this and decided to produce the film, and from that I produced the soundtrack and now I am writing the book!

Now that's what I'd call a career change, and I have loved every bit of it - don't get me wrong, these are massive steps in a different direction and very risky, and only you will be able to choose just which way you want to take your career. One thing is certain, what I'm doing now is not really a proper job in the eyes of my parents, but I couldn't be more at home!

Remember to think out of the box when deciding your next career move, as normal stuff will just bore the hell out of you, I can promise you that!

Another thing you may find is that it's not always the right choice to stay and work in the family business! Obviously we have established that this condition breeds entrepreneurs and small business owners, and these people grow the business with the goal of their children taking it over. In the past, this has always worked really well but in the modern world people with ADD ADHD usually have their own ideas and much bigger goals than just working in something which has already been created, and much prefer to go out and create their own business! A fresh new challenge and something that isn't likely to bore them to death!

Remember that if your parents have this condition there's a very good chance you will inherit it, and if so you will be very similar to them in everyday life! The trouble is you could be too similar, and end up clashing in the workplace. I've been in this situation as I worked for my parents for a good few years, but in the end I just knew I had to do it all on my own! Looking back it's the best thing I ever did and at least I still have a decent relationship with my parents, even though they think I do nothing for living and I'm lazy! Ha,ha!

Don't be frightened to do something that is completely out of your comfort zone, you will find that you can turn your hand to most things!

12. Hates of People with ADHD

Well where do I start on this one! We hate being told what to do!

We hate having to do things that we don't want to do.

We hate not being able to do something, and it frustrates us.

We hate anything that's boring or uninteresting, including people!

We hate queuing and waiting around!

We hate not getting our own way.

We hate people that don't let us speak!

We hate anyone who thinks they are gonna steal our show.

We hate Marmite - well doesn't everyone? (joke!)

We hate a normal nine to five job, and struggle to hold on to them.

We hate routine! We find it totally boring!

We hate doing the same thing over and over again!

We hate doing homework!

We hate getting bossed around and find it irritating.

We hate school exams, and can often get very stressed about them.

We hate being put under pressure, yet we often operate better when we are!

We hate being labelled as naughty!

We hate not being able to find a parking space.

We hate people who push and shove in clubs etc.

We hate people that butt into our conversation.

We hate drama queens.

We hate not being able to do something.

We hate being told directly to do something!

We hate people who talk over us!

We hate the thought of failure, it can be devastating.

We hate admitting when we are wrong.

We hate wasted time and have very little patience.

We hate admitting defeat or giving in.

We hate accepting the truth sometimes.

We hate being locked away and our movements being restricted.

We hate being told we cannot have something!

We hate doing pointless and uninteresting things.

We hate filling in any kind of official forms...ie tax returns etc.

We hate having to do the same thing over and over again.

We hate doing something that fails, not just work-anything.

We hate getting frustrated.

As you can see, there are many things that we hate, and there are many more things that frustrate us and get us wound up! We don't function when we are in the wrong place, and if there's a point at which that really starts to get to you, my best advice is to avoid it like the plague!

I'm sure that there are a lot of the above points that apply to you, and please don't think that they are just my personal hates. I have used a cross - section which generally applies to both males and females across the spectrum.

So how do we deal with our pet hates? We will usually bite the bullet and just dive straight in head-first, but we all know that there will always be a chance of failure when we do this.

If there's a way of doing something without actually involving any of your pet hates, then I suggest you try that way first, because by doing this you might just stop yourself from getting frustrated and wound up, and we all know that we achieve better results by staying calm, sometimes easier said than done!

The other way is to convince yourself that you don't actually hate it that much. This removal of a mental block is something that you seem to get better at with age, and it's a great feeling to actually achieve something that involves a pet hate, especially if you succeed at it. From this point on, that old pet hate is now something that doesn't bother you in the slightest!

Like most things that go with this condition, they can all be fixed, the thing is to convince yourself that you want to fix it.

MIND OVER MATTER is very important when it comes to your pet hates!

13. Arguments

People with ADD ADHD will almost certainly have more arguments than 'normals'. I have made myself a rule these days and always try to stick to it, the result being a lot less arguments, even if the odd ones I do have may be gigantic. I only argue when I know I'm 100% correct, and have no doubts about being wrong. Hang on! Isn't this what a person with ADHD does all the time? Yes - and you have to learn that you are not always right. I was the worst in the world for it to be honest, and now by sticking to my new method I definitely have a lot less arguments. On the other hand, as I will only argue when I know I'm right, I will enter into that argument and will not back down until proven right! Sometimes a fight will occur before a solution, but there's nothing worse than someone trying to tell you something that you know yourself is totally incorrect. You just have to prove them wrong!

Arguments between parents and siblings are all too common where the condition occurs, and some really do cause permanent damage to relationships (see section 2 family problems). Looking back, I am full of regrets about my family arguments and even now when I feel I'm in control of my ADHD, they still happen. I seem to have spent so much more time making up to people than I did causing the rifts in the first place and looking back it makes me very angry with myself!

Now I know a lot more about this condition I can see more clearly where I went so wrong, and luckily for me it's not too late to correct as many of those mistakes as I can. Some people don't have that privilege, and many of these silly family arguments are literally taken to the grave!

Your ability to argue will come in very handy during your lifetime and people with this condition are generally very good at it, as they love to get their own way!

I have set myself a very strict rule these days as I found myself getting in way too many arguments in the past. There was a point where I would happily jump into other peoples' conversation to point out the facts I felt they were getting wrong. I don't know quite why I did this, but knew that I had to change something and fast. I gave myself the rule...I only argue when I know I'm right one-hundred per cent, and because of this I would literally argue with people to the point of getting into fights! A little extreme maybe, but when someone is trying to tell you something and you are one hundred percent sure that you are in the right, it can become very annoying and get to a point where you will probably go a little further than you normally would!

Kids with ADHD are very bad for arguing, as they always seem to think they are right. Obviously this applies to adults as well, but they tend to become a little more chilled as they get older and just can't be bothered arguing, even if they know they are right. Unfortunately, it is something I still enjoy, and there's nothing I like more than a good argument, especially when I know I will end up winning it!

Quite often people with this condition will bottle things up inside till it gets to a point when they usually explode and all their thoughts on the subject usually come straight out. This is often how an argument starts, especially if it's between two people with ADHD, when sparks can really fly. This is a lot more obvious in families of course, as there's a good chance that there could be a few people in the same household with the same condition, and this really can lead to fiery times and lots of arguments!

It's just another example of how this condition can affect normal everyday family life as these arguments can actually end up destroying relationships and friendships.

Pick your arguments well, and try to argue only when you know you are right - that's good advice!

14. Entrepreneurs

As more and more people are becoming familiar with this condition, it is becoming very apparent that ADD ADHD breeds entrepreneurs and successful people. On the other side of the coin however it can also be the downfall of prospective entrepreneurs who bite off more than they can chew.

Have a good think about all of the successful people you know and then answer this question with honesty - do you think they are a little bit different? Do you think they might have ADHD? There's a massive possibility that they have either this condition or one of the ones connected to it!

I'll put money on it that most of them weren't very good at school either! I was very average at school, more interested in earning money in the lunch break than handing a project in! Unless it involved designing or creating something, I just wasn't interested in it, and found most subjects boring!

Richard Branson is a classic example of how to do it right and is definitely the best "rebel" millionaire/billionaire around. Here, my interpretation of rebel means that he takes on things that it's believed literally can't be done and usually make a massive success out of them, not that he does things wrong! Well, actually he does do things wrong, but this is exactly why he is so successful! These kinds of people think totally out of the box, are always keen to make change, to try new things and push the boundaries to the absolute limits of business, usually with massive success. Please don't presume that if you have ADD ADHD and you open a business that you are going to be a massive success, as it takes a lot of hard work, much sacrifice and a bit of luck to pull off your dream! Beware - the failure rate of people who venture into business with this condition is very high, and the ones that do succeed seem to really do it on a very big scale, everyone has to start somewhere though.

It's not all roses being an entrepreneur by the way, and there are many downsides to consider before you go putting everything on the line for an idea that might not work. An entrepreneur's life can be a very lonely one, and quite often it can cost you your marriage, so don't get too wrapped up in your work, and try to split the time well between you and your family!

Entrepreneurs are totally driven, but what is it gives them the drive that they have? I'm afraid to say it is self-doubt! They are always doubting themselves, which pushes them to succeed...ring any bells?

Usually a good entrepreneur has a great idea but not the funds to actually bring it to fruition, and this is where you might have to find an investor. You can fill an investor's head with all your ideas and I fear it won't make any difference to the decision whether to invest in your company or not, if you want to get your hands on the loot make sure you are full of self-confidence, as they will only invest in you, and not in your idea! You are basically selling yourself, and the best way to do that is by positive thinking! What happens if I fail? Quite simple: you will either pick yourself back up and dust yourself down and then carry on, or you could go down the lonely depression route, which I must warn can end up in suicide! Only you can decide if you think you have the skills to succeed as an entrepreneur, just remember the rewards are very high but the risk is usually higher!

I would class myself as an entrepreneur even though I am in a situation where I'm starting from scratch. I have just returned from a meeting with an investor and he turned up in a brand new yellow Lamborghini! The first thing I thought was "you lucky swine", but that thought soon changed into "maybe next year". The point I'm making is that there are many different levels of being an entrepreneur, from the level I was at last year raising the budget to make a film, to the high-flying businessman in a yellow Lamborghini that I met today! One thing is sure, you have to start somewhere, and how far you go is down to how much effort you put in and how much luck you have. Even the guy in a flash sports car started with nothing... and anything is possible if you put your mind to it! Good luck!

15. The Party Animal

I wonder how many of you reading this book are self-confessed party animals either now or in the past.

Speaking from personal experience and taking into account the behaviour of the people with ADHD who I've spent a lot of time with, I have come to the conclusion that we are all just mad for it! I can't remember ever leaving a party until the end (unless it was crap obviously!) and I certainly remember all the parties that I have organised myself - basically in a nut shell, we are a breed of party animals!

This has both good and bad points of course!

People who party are also prone to depression, and this is when the voices in the head and the addictions can become a problem again! Finding an appropriate balance is very hard, but as you get older your tendency to party does get a little less pronounced, so you might actually be able to avoid the mid - life crisis if you do manage to find the balance!

It is never a good sign when teenagers are partying a lot, as it tends to become a way of life and can literally take over! I used to live for the weekend, and gradually you can find that the weekends can actually begin to get longer and before you know it you're partying mid - week as well. My job these days involves lots and lots of parties but I don't just go and get wrecked five times a week, I wouldn't be able to handle that at my age! I have learnt to go out and drink water instead of Jack D and Coke constantly. Although I'm quite proud of myself for this, my situation is very different and I can't really drink whilst I'm doing my job anyway!

The more that I meet people in this industry the more I can see that most of them have ADD ADHD or similar. It seems that if you are good at partying the chances are you will be very good at organising parties.

As a teenager you are very vulnerable to drinking and partying, and it's not until you meet someone and have a serious relationship that there is any chance of this ending. There's also the problem that if your partner is into partying there's every chance your partying will continue together right up until you have children.

You are never too old to party by the way. Ibiza never ceases to amaze me and the age of people partying on this particular island is much higher than most of the other areas. It's as if they never want to grow up and you will quite often see people dancing away in the clubs who are in their 70s or even older, and personally I think this is great! I am definitely one of those breeds who just refuse to grow old and you will find this is common in very many people with ADHD.

Unfortunately for those of us that do have ADHD partying is not only a great release of your tension but it can also release your inner demons and what used to be a Saturday night knees-up can very easily turn into two or three days a week or more, until you get to a point where you find you are fighting partying addiction! You may laugh, but this can very easily lead to depression and addictions, and can be the start of a very bad period in your life.

The other thing to look out for when you are partying is the fact that everyone around you is usually drunk, and therefore a lot of things are often said in the heat of the moment - remember that you react in a totally different way when drinking, and so do others around you. Aggression, bad looks and even a spilt drink can easily end up in a fight and if you have a temper like I used to you will not walk away from these situations - in fact, quite the opposite - you are more likely to jump straight in and start lashing out! However the only thing this does is either land you in hospital or in big trouble with the police, don't make the mistakes I made in this area - it takes a bigger man to walk away than to get involved.

Partying is about having fun, and there's nothing better than getting home safe and sound after a great night out but you will always have to be on your guard, it's very easy for a great laugh to turn into something much worse. Go and enjoy your partying, it really can be the best time of your life, just make sure you live to tell everyone the stories of how wild you were, obviously I have lots to tell, ha!

16. The Nutter, or is he/she?

All of my life I have felt slightly different to most people, but I could never manage to put my finger on it until the day I found I had ADHD. Even during the making of 'Ibiza - My Way or the High Way', my director quite often referred to me as a nutter, obviously meaning this to be taken in a nice way - apparently!

A recurring phrase you might be familiar with is that there's a fine line between genius and insanity, and this is much more true than we have been made to believe! I am fortunate to be constantly in contact or working with what I believe to be some of the most talented people on the planet, especially when it comes to music and sport, and can honestly say that nearly all of them are barking mad in their own individual way. The links between ADD ADHD and a mild lunacy are all too apparent, but no-one has emphasised just how so many people with this condition are the best at what they do! Steven Spielberg, Tarantino and George Lucas are terrific examples! These three film directors have brought us without doubt some of the best films of all time.

There's no doubt this condition breeds geniuses, but wherever there's genius, there tends to lurk lunacy. Do a little bit of research yourselves, it should be easy enough - look at ten really successful people, some of whom you might know, some may already be famous and then re-examine their histories. I'll bet you all, or very nearly all are also a bit nuts!

This may seem controversial, but I suspect that Hitler and many of his henchmen had ADHD, as several were interested in strange Oriental cults and obscure philosophies. Quite likely, so do more 'acceptable' figures, like Bill Clinton and Ronald Reagan. I see a pattern which I feel sure might have been seen before but never really spoken about. It definitely looks that a very high percentage of the really successful - for good or evil - people in this world are actually a bit crackers!

I'm quite proud to be a bit nuts, life is always interesting, my hunger for adventure and the will to win combine to make the proper foundations for a fully classified nutter. Chuck in a few crazy ideas and a little bit of genius and before you know it you have the perfect looney!

The problem with the word 'nutter' is that it is used across a very large spectrum and quite often refers to people who are totally out of control, which is not the bracket I see myself in, as these days I like to think I'm firmly in control - at least most of time anyway!

People associate 'nutter' with mental hospitals these days but believe me there are plenty of very clever nutters around, and these people go on to be very successful across the whole spectrum of life.

Sometime being a little bit nuts will stand you in good stead. Sometimes you have to push things a little further than most would just to get results. If you look at a moto-cross champion for example, they have to take massive risks to become ultra successful, and even I would class some of these riders as total nutters, but they are fully in control and just usually a lot more talented than the rest....and remember these are people with ADHD.

Use your intuition and judge for yourself who you think may be nuts, you might find that these are the kind of people you mix with much better - as they say, it takes one to know one! Personally I can only be around people that are a bit different, or nuts as some would call them, the trouble is that 'normal' people just bore me to a point of suicide and I try to spend as little time as possible with this strange breed of human!

Who wants to be boring? Not me, thanks!

Section 5

1. One for the Road

Always the last to leave the party! How many times have we heard this one, "fancy one more?" – this is simply one of the worst things you can say to someone with ADD ADHD.

Whether it be one more game of pool or one more round of drinks, it's one of the hardest things for people with this condition to do - just to say no! Although sometimes it may be a struggle to get a person with ADD ADHD to go out on a night out, beware! actually getting them home before morning can prove pretty well impossible, especially if a 'session' is in the offing. Any person with this condition will recognise just how much we like going on an extended session and more to the point, how much we hate leaving it! The session is an extended opportunity to show off, to impress friends and strangers alike, to hold court and be centre of attention secure in the knowledge that no-one's going anywhere in a hurry! Perfect! It's an open goal, it's you one-on-one with the keeper, clear through and the ref about to blow the whistle, it's glory staring you in the face, your last - well, latest - stab at immortality!

More mundane perhaps, but this same principle also applies to something as simple as the last drink. How many times have you been in a bar, knowing that you had to be somewhere else and someone popped that fatal question 'one for the road?' and more importantly, how many times have you actually said no? If you're anything like me, not very many!

Obviously and inevitably, the seemingly insignificant last drink can cause all sorts of difficulties for you and those around you. Family problems are often caused in such situations as people are either late home or don't come home at all, resulting in a lot of stress and arguments. You may be late back to work if it's a lunchtime drink, which could lead to at least a reprimand - and we have seen how we react to that form of discipline! - or worse still, that one last drink could also lead to you being over the legal limit to drive, which could result in you losing your licence, your job and then in turn maybe your family! Almost before you know it, you're unemployed and having 'one for the road' all day, everyday!

Although I have cited alcohol in the above examples, the same endgame can be caused by drugs. One more line! How many people actually have the willpower to say no when they have a line of cocaine put in front them? Not that many, I think.

Another classic example of one for the road can apply to your working patterns, would you believe. I have been writing solidly now for about six hours and keep going over the personal deadline that I previously set myself. When things are flowing, it's very hard to stop, and this doesn't just refer to a stream of alcohol, it also applies to work. I keep telling myself I must stop, then hear a voice telling me to go on for just another page, and here I still am at daft o'clock, working by candlelight, so to speak. The good thing lies in the positive progress that can be made when you're in a groove, so here's the point...

'One for the road' should be exactly that when it is set in a negative context, but if something seems good and you feel on a roll, then that 'one for the road' is probably a gamble worth taking - after all, that impulsive, instinctive being is exactly who we are, and as long as we are achieving great results we tend to okay it with ourselves! Just make sure you okay it with your wife or husband too, otherwise 'one for the road' might just be what you are doing in the divorce courts!

To the true gambler, one for the road can be the nail in the coffin. Roulette is infamous for keeping people at the table for one more spin and most people increase their bet on what is intended as their last spin, usually a losing one and then it's a case of trying to win it back, hence one for the road in the casino very rarely actually turns out to be just that. Most of the time, the only reason someone leaves a casino is because they have spent all their cash!

Our addictive personality can prove fatal when put in the one for the road situation, and that applies equally to drink, drugs, gambling and even to work.

As you master your ADHD you must teach yourself to remember that 'one for the road' is fine, as long as it is exactly that. Too many times 'one for the road' ends up as just one too many!

2. ADHD... I Wish

No one in their right mind would wish to have something 'wrong' with them, would they? Apparently so and the day this was brought to my attention was the day my opinion on this condition changed forever! We were on the roof of our house in Spain watching the sunrise after a long night out, I suppose you could say we were carrying on the party. As we have established, we ADD ADHD 'sufferers' are *the* party animals who just don't know when to stop!

After dancing around for a couple of hours, we woke the whole neighbourhood up and before we knew it we had crowds of people out on their balconies watching us - obviously we simply carried on, as no-one was gonna tell us to stop the party ha,ha!

One guy in particular was taking a bigger interest than others and I went to the roof and had a conversation with him. He shook my hand and thanked us for the entertainment telling me how crazy we were - in the nicest possible way. I asked him if he had heard of ADHD and he replied "yes", so I then asked him if he thought he might have it himself, his reply nearly made me fall off the roof!..."I WISH!" is what he said! Totally shocked by his answer, I asked him why? And he replied, "BECAUSE ITS A TOTAL GIFT!" As you will know by now, this was the title of an earlier section in the book, so I suppose you can see where I got the idea for the title now.

I couldn't stop thinking afterwards about what this guy had said to me, and as it started to sink in, it also started to change my own personal opinions of ADHD. You may have had a difficult childhood, you might have struggled more than others at school but something that has always hampered you in the past might actually turn out to be a gift! I'm a firm believer that ADHD *is* a gift, but only if you learn how to control it, thereby enabling you to control yourself a lot better in the future! This doesn't take long by the way! Maybe just reading this book, and maybe another in order to get a slightly different perspective, could just be enough to unlock the secret to future success in dealing with your condition.

It was by reading a book similar to this one that changed everything for me, and once again positive thinking, combined with a new angle on life and maybe some different views on events and situations, and you will begin to see yourself have a lot more success, even if it is only dealing with everyday matters! Something like that can be so difficult for a person living with ADD ADHD.

One thing I have to add here is that although this condition might appear a gift to some people, there will inevitably be only a small percentage of people go on to be very successful, and while a very high proportion hold important jobs, there will always be a percentage who fail to reach their goal and end up with their lives in pieces. One thing is for sure - that all of the above have gone through a lot that the 'normals' will never encounter to get to where they are, and most of them would just love to have a 'normal' day! I know I long for just one such day in my life, but for some reason they seem to escape me!

It's on days like today that I feel totally thankful for having ADHD, as strange as that may sound. We are currently in the process of editing the film, and it entails working very long hours and is very stressful, and at times I just don't know how I can divide my time equally between that and the book as well, but in reality I do know. It is exactly because of this mental condition we call ADHD.

I have been working now for sixteen hours, stopping only for toilet breaks and one meal, whilst making about fifty phone calls and sending as many emails. Basically, the "hyperfocus" button has been pressed in solidly all day and most of tonight as well. What this has enabled me to do is literally the work of four days and it's situations like this that make us stand out from the 'normals'!

It is also how we breed so many successful entrepreneurs, the ones who will work all the hours and take the risks to get the job done! Given the choice, in this context most "normals" would give anything to have this facility, and you must trust me on that one!

Right now though, my mind is swollen and my body hurts, and I think this is always the right point to throw in the towel and go to bed - night, night!

3. Depression

Although I'm not a doctor and not qualified in any way, shape or form, I have watched many of my close friends suffer with depression and have suffered badly with it myself.

Someone, somewhere, will hopefully take away something really useful from this section of the book, and you have to listen to me, please, when I say that you don't need anti-depressants to combat ADHD. It annoys me greatly that certain doctors give out such prescriptions left, right and centre without proper diagnosis.

We as a group are very vulnerable to depression, and this works in some very strange ways. As I've said, I always write parts to this book when I feel in the right mood for the particular section at hand, and right now feels just perfect! Check this out for a real-life example that happened just today!

I'm having a few problems with the film and need to get to final editing meetings, but can't even afford the flights, and I felt some negative pressure yesterday which generally made me feel very down. I woke up this morning still in a really bad mood, with stress levels much higher than normal. In such a situation we often find ourselves in the throes of a very slight depression, the day can go either way and it's usually out of your hands - well, mine went totally the wrong way!

I decided that instead of moping around I would go to town to get the last of my Christmas presents, as I thought this might help clear my head a bit, because it felt like everything around me was squeezing me. I drove the four miles there only to circle the town without finding a parking space, and all the time this is going on my head is working overtime, reading all sorts of things into the situation and generally making my own life very hard. Despite writing a book trying to help people deal with situations like this, I find my day spiralling out of control, and the more I try to calm down, the more I get myself in a twist. I had to stop for petrol, one of my pet hates as I've said, then to stop at a cash machine, and by this time the only place I wanted to be was on the couch at home. I had to head there immediately, and subsequently spent two hours on the couch being miserable to myself, not wanting to engage with anyone or anything. This mood has carried through till now, and only after typing for ten minutes am I beginning to calm down a little.

I call such days mini-depressed days as they don't last very long, and I find little everyday things, like going for a walk or something, can help prevent or stop them! Everyone deals with days like this in their own way and I must admit I was very surprised to find myself having one of these low days when in general everything in my life is in reality pretty much perfect right now. The big problem arises when you start to string these days together, because before you know it you can be in full scale depression. And the longer it lasts, the worse it gets. It can literally grab hold of you in a similar way that an addiction grabs hold, the difference being that while we tend to like the addictive things, no-one enjoys being depressed. This may be when you think a trip to doctor is what you need, but I would think very carefully about that one if I were you! He/she will most likely ask you a couple of questions before proceeding to write out a prescription which could easily send you to Mars, until they get the dosage correct! I hate prescription drugs so much that I won't even take an Aspirin or Paracetamol to cure a headache anymore. Ask yourself a question: How many people who commit suicide are taking prescription drugs at the time of their death? I'll wager the figure is very high, and I wouldn't even like to put a percentage on this one, as I feel it could well be so high it could cause me trouble with the medical profession.

So, we have gone from having a bad day to life on prescription drugs and thereby struggling to make it off the couch in the space of a couple of weeks. This is how easy it is for someone with ADD ADHD to fall into depression and in extreme circumstances this can without doubt lead to suicide. One statistic I found particularly interesting is that girls suffer from ADHD depression three times more than boys. Is this something to do with having a negative self-image, brought on by the relentless pressure created by the advertising industry?

Try to keep yourself in a positive mood, and avoid slipping into depression if at all possible! People with this condition are much more prone to depression than 'normals', so be very careful and at all costs avoid the easy route of going to the pub! Any problems will still be there when you get home!

4. Addictions

In case you hadn't already noticed, people with ADD ADHD have hugely addictive personalities, which can often be a major problem as most of the 'good things' in life aren't always the correct choices!

Don't think for one minute that 'normals' don't get addicted to things, because they do, the difference being that they don't get addicted to things quite so easily, or so badly! Earlier in the book you will have read the section on willpower, and there is a huge connection between willpower and addictions, as having the strength to say NO to something we like is one of the hardest things to do for a person with ADD ADHD, and quite often we just give in to these situations. I'm sorry to say that you will have to fight these demons for the rest of your life, and although it's very possible to beat addictions, it's not as easy to choose what you get addicted to, as no-one plans to get addicted to things!

Before you jump to the conclusion that this section is all about drugs and substances, keep reading and I'm sure you will be surprised to see that there's a lot more things out there to tempt you, that you would never think could do you damage, but you couldn't be more wrong! In fact, some things that can get you addicted are only simple things that most of us use every single day, coffee being the one that most readily springs to mind and, probably more seriously, tobacco. I have lost count of my attempts to quit smoking cigarettes, and although I publicly hold that it's a piece of cake and I can pack in anytime I decide, when it comes to the crunch, I just haven't yet been able to. This is a form of denial, I realise. Coffee addiction for me comes and goes, but cigarette addiction is there with me always, and I've tried everything!

Another one to watch out for is internet addiction, and again on a more serious note, on-line gambling. I have spent time addicted to online gambling (see 'Red or Black' section) and it almost certainly cost me my first marriage and contributed to me losing all of my shops. People with ADD ADHD are prone to gambling addiction, and the only advice I can give you on this is to not bother with it at all! The buzz of winning is one thing that we all enjoy but I'm afraid the constant desire to win when it comes to gambling makes it very addictive indeed. I have seen many lives totally ruined through gambling and it remains one of the biggest downfalls for people with this condition.

Obviously it is narcotics that cause the biggest problem for the person with ADD ADHD, always looking for the next buzz or high. Many people often turn to drugs, and this can have disastrous consequences. Cocaine is one of the most addictive drugs on the planet and I'm not ashamed to tell you this from experience. Like any addiction, you don't realise you're addicted until you try or succeed in stopping. The trouble with coke is that it is firstly very expensive but secondly very widely available, and especially if you have ADD ADHD you run the risk of running up serious debt and your life can quickly spiral out of control, even though you may not recognise the fact. Like gambling, cocaine is another thing that I recommend you completely stay away from - find something to replicate or approximate the buzz that coke gives you, only you can decide what might replace this major demon in the life of the person with the condition.

There are probably many more things to try and keep away from, but the next one may surprise you! Sex can be a major problem for a person with ADD ADHD, we can very easily get addicted to sex and this is where sexual boundaries are pushed to the limit. Again this is something you should be very conscious of, as pushing sexual boundaries can cause problems in your home life - I'm not suggesting you don't have sex, but just keep it real! I will go into more detail on this subject in the "Kinky Stuff" section later.

Another one that might shock you at first is how badly people can get addicted to energy drinks like Red bull and Monster, but again it is one of those where you just deny it and tell yourself you're not dependent on them. Add up how many you drink and then ask yourself the question - you may be surprised! As crazy as it may sound, I found myself totally addicted to green apple Lucozade, to the point where I used to buy it from a wholesaler in bulk! You might well laugh, but I think I later realised where my teeth went! I used to go through about ten bottles at my worst point, as I believed it gave me more energy to get through the day!... doh!

As if someone with ADHD needs an artificial blast of energy? Looking back, I was definitely addicted in a big way so once again, be very careful! Keep those energy drinks for when you're having vodka! Now there's a combo that really does hit the spot!

Beware...people with ADD ADHD are very addictive personalities, and you will need to use a great deal of willpower to keep control in all these areas!

5. Hero To Zero

You are the entrepreneur, the magician, the person who can pull off things that most others can't, the one who can rise to fame and fortune in a very short space of time! Well let me tell you, you can easily fall from a pedestal just as quickly as you got there and the fall will be nowhere near as enjoyable as the rise to success was!

Once a person with ADD ADHD pushes the self destruct button the only ones that can help them are our old mate William Power, some good friends and family and something to look forward to. We are the best types of human on the planet at destroying everything we have dreamed of and worked for, in a short period of time. We are impulsive and thrill-seeking, and when you combine these two together the odds suddenly stack up against you.

Another thing to watch out for is not only a big fall from grace but, in plain speaking, turning into a cock! If you ever get to the stage where you have a fanbase, there's nothing more upsetting for a fan than actually realising that the person that they idolise is actually just some knobhead in real life!

During my rallying career I got to the point where I had to sign the odd autograph and did a few TV appearances here and there, but even this low-level fame felt like a massive blanket around me, and it's easy to start to drift away from reality. I had to watch some very close friends who got a bit more famous than me turn into the most obnoxious shits, and it isn't long until this attitude starts to come across during interviews and public appearances. The minute the press or fans start to get a whiff of this is when all your problems will start, and could very well be the start of your fall from Hero to Zero.

I'm glad to say that all the people I knew then that became famous have now matured a lot, and experience does teach you that it is always best just to be yourself, as the ones who put an act on, are usually the ones who get caught out! This is why so many teenage stars end up pressing the self-destruct button not too long into their careers - don't get me wrong, they may have the right people around them to help in these situations and some do get through it, but there's no concealing the fact that so many just drift by the wayside.

Depression, alcohol, drugs, gambling, affairs - the list goes on, these are all the demons that can lead you off your path to stardom and even when you are there, they can all help to push you off.

From Hero to Zero can also apply in sport and even in everyday jobs, too. People with ADD ADHD don't handle rejection very well, and this is exaggerated greatly if you have been in a high profile place at some point, where everyone loved you and then suddenly you find you must deal with an entirely different world, one in which everyone doesn't love or worship you. These absolute opposites can be enough to drive someone to the end of their tether, and for people with this condition, these bad places are not good places to be!

Whatever your quest, whether it be a mission in life, like a professional sports career, or just a new job, always remember where you came from, and never forget your roots! It has been the downfall of many people and will be the downfall of many more in the future, I'm sure.

6. Why Didn't You Say Something?

Why is it that with something as serious as a mental condition, and in view of the fact that 50% of the 'cure' lies in knowing that you have it, why oh why are we always the last to find out? This is one of my main drives in raising peoples' awareness on this issue, as I had never even heard of the condition until a friend handed me a book on it and insisted I read it. I had only read one book since leaving school, but instantly found this book very interesting as so much of it applied to my situation. I'm hoping that whoever gets to read this book will have a similar experience to mine on the day I found out I had ADHD, and I am also hoping that many of you will go on to see your lives change for the better because of reading it.

How can a condition that is approximately one-hundred-years-old be so well-hidden and unpublicised, and more to the point, so badly diagnosed? Don't get me wrong, things seem to be getting a lot better, and I'm hopefully doing my bit to make it even better still in this respect, and maybe one day this condition will be known and recognised by a lot more people and understood by doctors a lot more, because personally I feel that lots of doctors are out of touch when it comes to ADD ADHD.

My life changed forever the day that I read the book in question, and I will always remember exactly how and when this happened. There was a piece in the book which talked about the "fire in the belly", and literally a second after reading this very important paragraph, it gave me the confidence to go out and attempt to live my dream!

This book, combined with others widely available, will offer you and your family alternative information on this condition, and it's much easier to come to terms with ADD ADHD if your family and friends are on the same wavelength.

Unfortunately for me, my whole family just thought I had lost the plot when I started rambling on about ADHD, and this has lots of very negative effects on how you deal with it. I just kept pressing on with my dreams whilst researching the condition every single day - something I continue to do on a daily basis. This is the reason why I felt compelled to write this book, as I feel I have lots of information and experiences to share with both individuals affected by the condition and with their families and, like when my doctor said to me, "you know more about this condition than me, Scott!", and I nearly fell off the chair at the realisation he wasn't joking, this really cheesed me off, and continues to do so, if I'm being honest!

Only last year, sitting with one of my best friends, I told him that I had a mental condition called ADHD, and he informed me he had known for years but just didn't know how to tell me.

Since finding out about this condition I am constantly wondering just how different my life could have been if I had known earlier, and I'm hoping this book will help people learn about a condition that not only affects them but also the people around them. Remember it is a lifelong condition that can be life-threatening and can cause major problems to you and your family, which needs to be taken very seriously even in adulthood, and the way that best helps in coping with it is by all around you knowing that you have it! This also applies to children who, if taught from a young age should be able to lead a totally normal life, and go on possibly to live their dreams, whatever those may be!

One of the ideas behind this book is to wake everyone up to this condition and for many parents reading this, to help their kids after realising they probably have the condition themselves. I was thirty-seven years of age when I found out - certainly no kid - and it's taken me a while to get my head around it, so prepare yourself for a bit of a shock when you find out, but by accepting that after the realisation things will become much clearer, you might find your quality of life also gets better.

If you feel someone close to you has this condition, my advice is to let them know like my friend did to me, but as soon as possible! Only then will they be able to start to deal with it a day at a time - we know there's no cure as such and it's life long, so it really is up to you to work out what's best for you and whoever you might think has the condition.

There are plenty of online tests which should give you enough information to then approach your GP who can then refer you to a specialist if need be. Don't let the doctors talk you round, which they will try to in my experience. It's as if they don't want the extra headache of dealing with this condition and its difficult effects - but maybe that just applies to the ones that I have seen!

The main rule arising from this section is to be totally proud of who and what you are, and if you have got ADD ADHD remember that in places these days it is being recognised as a gift and talent, so go out to enjoy and use it to its full effect!!

7. Suicide

As stated previously, it doesn't take a rocket scientist to see the massive links between ADD ADHD and suicide, yet it is something that officials don't seem to recognise and if they do, they certainly are not doing much about it!

I have lost two very close friends and one best mate to suicide, and after learning about this condition I began to see that they and many others in their situation very likely had ADD ADHD. The trouble is, their doctors had told them they had depression and filled them with wacky prescription drugs. When you combine these crazy pills with alcohol the effects can be devastating and sometimes fatal. I'm deeply sorry to say that I know these situations only too well and don't ever recall a happy outcome yet, the best way to prevent anything like this happening to you is simply to not take the prescription drugs. I myself have quite often taken Valium in the past as it definitely helped to calm me down and get to sleep, but the trouble is they are very addictive, and before you know it you can be taking them every day just to get to sleep!

As you move up the ladder of prescription drugs, the more mind-altering they get, and I suspect you may be asking yourself what this has got to do with suicide. Of those people I knew who decided to take their life, all were on some sort of prescribed drug, and I have seen a definite pattern emerge. People with ADD ADHD need to keep narcotics to an absolute minimum, as they are by nature in great danger of becoming dependant on them.

I have also looked into suicide statistics and found that the islands that I have referred to regularly in this book are full of people with ADD ADHD and both islands have a very high suicide rate!

I remember sitting on the edge of the sixth storey of the car park in the Isle of Man which my friend had jumped off a few years before. I could hear voices in my head telling me to jump too, but luckily right at the last second another voice came along and I snapped back into the real world, a split-second decision, but my life could have been over! Saved by the voices in my head, and I was totally sober and straight-headed, imagine what could have happened if I was full of prescription drugs, it doesn't bear scrutiny! All I know for sure is how glad I am that I didn't jump, others haven't got to think about it afterwards but one thing is certain, their families will think about it every day for the rest of their days!

If you are ever sat in the same position that I was on that dreadful day, and hearing nasty voices in your head (common in this condition), try to hear your parents' voices in there and stop to think what you are about to do to them, don't ever be so selfish as to think of suicide as an option when things are bad! Remember this! There is always somebody worse off than you!

Ironically, only two hours after I'd finished writing this came news that the famous footballer and manager Gary Speed had been found hanged at his home. Forty-two years old, wife, two teenage kids, a multimillionaire and the manager of the Wales international football team, he was also an Everton legend.

What drives a person with so much going for them to do something like this? ADHD I fear, the voices in the head I speak of.

I don't know what situation led Gary Speed to kill himself, but one thing I do know is that in his mind at that particular moment, whatever problems he perceived in his head must have been so great that he felt no other option existed other than to take his own life.

Another sad end to a young life and another statistic that largely backs up what I have discovered about the link between ADHD and suicide I'm afraid.

Many professional footballers have ADHD, but some can learn to live and deal with it.

RIP Gary Speed.

8. Red or Black

The gambler, the chancer, the red devil and the black knight all in one - gambling is like the annus horribilis of ADHD!

It's in our nature to take risks and push the boundaries of life to achieve the ultimate buzz, but it's a sad fact that gambling is one of the worst addictions for a person with ADD ADHD. And especially internet gambling! Now professional poker players aside, there's no one in the world who actually wins at gambling! There might be the odd respite, but in the end there is only ever one winner in this industry. The casino owners or machine owners, you can't win, it's really as simple as that! No doubt you think that you will break the mould and can confound history and experience by winning, as that's ADHD all over - what if? Or you may be asking when? And the answer is never!

I got to be completely hooked on internet gambling, and it lasted for at least three years, it cost me my first marriage and it helped lead to the downfall of my businesses. It turns you into a liar, it makes you very dishonest and brings misery to all around you. It also takes hold of people with ADHD much more easily than 'normals', so you have to be very careful indeed! In fact if you want my advice, it's much better not to gamble at all! I wish I had never started, because now the only way I can stay away from it is to never go to casinos, and that's the bit I miss most! You will notice the early signs of this addiction in teenage kids with fruit machines, and it can cause big problems even from a very young age. Kids can also get addicted and they will steal just to gamble, just like the drug or alcohol addicted, so as I said earlier, just don't do it! Once you start, it's very hard to stop!

"Red or black" doesn't just apply to gambling with money incidentally! I used to be a nutter on a BMX bike and once jumped over 14 people off a 45 gallon drum with a door on it. Thinking back it was a stupid thing to do, as although I felt the buzz of making the jump, not once did I think how much I might hurt myself or of the safety of others for that matter? This is the kind of gamble that people with ADD ADHD take all day, every day!

Obviously it doesn't always involve jumping people on a bike, but even down to simple things like crossing the road, it's a fact that people with ADD ADHD are at greater danger of being run over by cars! This is a proven fact and one that you should think about each and every time you cross the road! We just don't concentrate, it's as simple as that, we are clumsy and a danger to ourselves, and this is another aspect of the condition that you will have to get to grips with!

Now I wouldn't wish to pry, but do you take the odd gamble in the bedroom? I'll bet you do!

One piece of really good advice I gave earlier was to not gamble at all! This is particularly applicable when it comes to bedroom antics, as your playful thoughts could very well land you in hot water! People with ADHD are very naughty in the bedroom and I would stick my neck out and say that men are worse than women.

Don't let your slightly twisted mind start telling you that all of your thoughts when it comes to sex are the same as your partner's, as you could well be very disappointed and, once a situation arises where the wrong impression is given, then it can be the start of the downfall of a marriage or relationship.

Will she? Won't she (or he)? ...this is one gamble where the stakes are very high indeed! ...an ultimate buzz situation - the one thing that we crave so much! But which could lead to ultimate disaster, the very thing that we handle so badly!

Now don't get me wrong, if the odds are stacked in your favour and it's looking like a dead cert, then go for it! Just be prepared that your little gamble may just not pay off!!

I don't think I will ever stop being a gambler, but would like to think that I now choose what I'm going to gamble on very carefully. I avoid fruit machines, keep out of casinos, and don't play anything online. But I'm an entrepreneur, one of the maddest you will ever meet and must keep my gamblers instinct if I am to have any chance of fulfilling my dreams of building a world famous brand! When it comes to business, everything is a gamble, the difference is I get to pick my games and to make the odds, and when you take that into account, I have always got a better chance of winning!

Try to reduce your odds in all situations, and the less you gamble, the more chance you have of avoiding getting addicted to it...spend your money wisely, it makes far more sense!

9. The Kinky Stuff

Throughout this book you've heard all sorts of things, some cheery and some not, so I have saved a section that might cheer you up till right at the end.

One area where most people with ADD ADHD totally excel is in the bedroom, - or the car, the garden, a field, or even behind the bike sheds, after all we are supposed to be the kinky percentage of the human race.

We are renowned for having a huge sexual appetite and have been known to get up to all sorts of antics in the sack! Obviously this isn't all good and there are many pitfalls you have be careful of if you are to succeed as the Casanova you fervently wish to be.

Males are very prone to falling victim of these pitfalls, and we forever hear of men being unfaithful, with often devastating results. Families fall apart, parents separate, and the children are often left to be brought up in single families. The phrase 'keep it your pants' comes to mind at this point.

Alcohol is usually a major factor in men or women having affairs and because of the mojo of a person with ADHD bad situations often arise, they love the chase and they love the danger. The more dangerous the situation, the better it feels very often, but what you won't be thinking about are the consequences.

As in other situations, people with ADD ADHD are instantly full of regret after doing something they know they shouldn't have. My good friend William Power is who you need to call on when faced with these situations, and I strongly advise you to listen to him! What's the point of ruining so many peoples' lives just to have sex with someone? This lesson is something you will only be able to teach yourselves as the situation arises, I'm afraid.

The next problem to feature in the kinky section is the will of people with ADD ADHD to push the boundaries of sex to the max! You could be a sucker for anything naughty and if you fall into that category, please beware! Before you know it you may be taking part in orgies or possibly wife-swapping!

Now each to their own and all that, but while these things might seem great at the time, they can make a relationship suffer in the blink of an eye.

One of the funniest things I heard whilst in conversation with a load of nutters in Ibiza was the phrase, "danger wank". I remember falling about laughing at the time and didn't even know what it was meant to signify, even though I suppose it's a bit self-explanatory! Of course, I had to ask - just to make sure I was on the right track! The reply was as funny as I'd imagined, this one guy in particular was only too happy to tell the group how he achieved the ultimate buzz by going somewhere he shouldn't and pleasuring himself. Evidently this is where the phrase "danger wank" came from. I asked him what would have happened if he'd got caught, and he told me that it was this that made him do it in the first place. Some people have some strange ways of getting their sexual kicks, but one thing I would say is approach anything in the kinky section with extreme caution.

People with this condition will always push sexual boundaries and before you know it, you may end up appearing in a low-budget porno film! Am I just exaggerating again? Well, what I really mean is you could end up in very hot water for doing a random thing which nine times out of ten you will regret the next day, or for even longer if you get caught!

People with ADD ADHD just love to dress up, and shops like the Anne Summers chain could have been created just for us! Apparently we can be very fond of role playing games, and are always on the lookout for the kinky buzz to satisfy our sex-fuelled fantasies?

I couldn't possibly personally verify the above by the way as it would be giving too much away - ha ha!

Another one to watch out for is online porn and chatrooms. Internet porn and web rooms are something that most will do for a laugh at first, but beware as you can very easily become addicted to online porn!

In short - be very careful with your sexual fantasies, as they could just come back round and bite you on the bum! Mmm! ...kinky!

10. I'm Not Gay...am I?

Let's recall one of the statistics here, that 80% of people with ADD ADHD are bi-curious. I struggle to believe this one to be honest, but it has it come from a environment? However having said this, my research is beginning to suggest that even if this figure isn't quite accurate, the proof is in the pudding so to speak, and I haven't come across many people that are gay, men or women, that don't show the signs of ADD ADHD. I would love to know exactly what percentage of the population is actually gay or bi-sexual? If we bear in mind that approximately 10% of the population has ADD ADHD, wouldn't it be a bit unusual if a similar proportion of the human race wasn't actually gay or bi-curious?

I have already mentioned that Ibiza seems to have the highest rate of ADD ADHD I have ever seen or heard of anywhere on the planet, and we have proof that people with this condition can have sexuality issues - would it be far-fetched to suggest that Ibiza should technically have a massive gay population?

Well it has! Ibiza town is classed as the gay capital of the world and there are more gay people than straight people there, not that surprising in view of its up-front hedonism, but very interesting food for thought nonetheless.

Don't start panicking and jumping to any conclusions here incidentally - there's still plenty of hedonism to go round, enough for everyone regardless of their sexual preferences!

How do I know about this, as one in the 20% bracket? In the circles I mix in, I get to know lots and lots of gay people and the more I think on the matter, I can't think of one gay person I've met that hasn't the signs of ADD ADHD. Think about some gay people that you know, or use some famous examples - Elton John, Kenny Everett, Alan Carr...these individuals are all openly gay and in my opinion are full of ADHD as well, the more people I think of, the more this fact seems to become obvious and I really believe there's a glut of evidence to back this up as fact!

Where does this leave straight people with ADD ADHD? You tell me! Maybe we are all a little more gay than we thought? Maybe this is another reason why it takes many years and such difficulty for someone to "come out", and why there are so many men who have children who later realise they're gay, and of course the same would also apply to women!

I reckon that despite the 80/100% statistic quoted, there are more straight people with ADHD than gay people so technically you can continue your life, whatever that may entail, in the knowledge that having this condition won't affect your sexuality in any way. Having said that I do know plenty of people that have done exactly the opposite, fretting constantly about the way people perceive them! ...maybe we are not so safe from this as we'd care to believe? Either way, only you will know what sexuality you are, but a word of warning here! We aren't all fortunate enough to live in a liberal environment, each to their own may seem a natural standpoint to adopt, but doesn't make you any less vulnerable to those who would live your life for you!

It's also said how happy and fun gay people can be, but they can frequently have a really fiery side to them and it's said there tends to be a 'male' and a 'female' type in a gay relationship. One is generally quite bossy and the other is usually a bit more laid back but equally as stubborn, which can lead to fiery relationships. Does any of the above ring true? I believe it will... and this is why I'm convinced that most gay people who have come out of the closet do actually have ADD ADHD, and one reason they are happy with themselves is because they don't care what other people think of them, and neither should we. This is typical in the behaviour of someone with ADHD, a rule-breaker who is totally happy to be different from the rest –especially once they have gained full control of their condition!

11. Jobs Linked to ADHD

There is a very good reason why I decided to include this section in the book. It was after discovering one of the worst statistics I have heard about the condition. I was told by a specialist that I went to see that 68% of people with ADD ADHD don't make the general workforce and I very nearly cried. And because of this I have begun to write a list of jobs that I know to have a high percentage of people with this condition working in that field.

Job satisfaction is an absolute must for people with ADD ADHD, as if their work isn't stimulating enough for their brain they will just get bored! People with this condition need to feel a constant sense of achievement, and this is one of the reasons why so many become small business owners and some even full blown entrepreneurs! This condition breeds good leaders and business people, and that's a recognised fact!

If there are any that I have missed, please accept my apologies in advance, but the ones below are the ones that readily come to mind:

Personal trainers

Architects

Policemen and women

Lawyers

Film directors

Film producers

The entertainment industry

Top sports professionals

Doctors and nurses

Scientists

Comedians

Artists

Entrepreneurs

Bosses and Team Leaders

Bodybuilders/weight lifters

Travelling jobs/funfairs

Market traders

Car dealers

Joiners/construction industry

Craftsmen

Dressmakers

Fighter pilots

Rescue workers

Writers/producers

Rock stars

Musicians

Members of Parliament

Teachers

Instructors

Stuntmen

Magicians

Gamblers

Poker players

Stock brokers

Disc jockeys

Actors/actresses

Escorts and models

Vicars and priests

Drug dealers

Insurance salespeople

Don't panic by the way if there's nothing in the above that suits or appeals to you!

People with ADD ADHD can learn many different trades, the forty years old mark seems to be a very big turning point for adults with the condition. For some reason we seem to start the approach to this landmark age with the full intention of turning our lives totally upside down and setting out on a new career.

I think it's probably because deep down in our hearts we mostly feel like we have underachieved, which is very common in our group by the way and can quite often lead to depression. Failure to people with ADD ADHD is just unthinkable, and one problem in today's climate is it's very hard to succeed in business, so only the strong or the lucky ones will actually make it, especially if they choose to open their own business.

However, don't be discouraged! The percentage of people with their own businesses who have a history of this condition in the family is in fact very, very high! You will always struggle to take orders from people in positions above you and when you stack up all the odds there's a damn good chance you will end up being your own boss someday!

Don't be frightened! It's the best job in the world being your own boss and will give you a whole different outlook on life! Go for it!! ...what's the worst that can happen? You could lose everything? Most people who end up millionaires have lost everything at some point in their lives, for whatever reason, and when you hit forty it is as if you have all the experience and life-skills in the world to do something successful - so get up off yer arse and start choosing a career that you want to do and stop doing the one you feel that you have to do! You are better than that, make no mistake!

12. The Fire in the Belly

The good old 'fire in the belly' - that signal when your body tells you to do something, whether it be something that merely generates a quick buzz, or something that changes your life forever!

This fire in the belly is not always a good thing to experience, what you need to be careful of is what you do when you get this great urge to do something different. I was sat reading a book, "The DaVinci Method", and there was a great moment for me, a piece in the book that as soon as I had read it, my life changed forever. One little sentence that made all the negative thoughts that I had about myself turn into this hot feeling inside my stomach, sending clear messages to my brain telling me to "go for it". It was at this point exactly when I made the decision to learn how to DJ and go to Ibiza looking for stardom. Here is a small extract from that very page:

"As you progress in finding your true self, you will experience "callings" to pursue certain endeavours. Maybe it's a new career or a new hobby, a new cause or a new family. Whatever the calling is, it will haunt you until you answer the call. When you answer the call, your life will shift dramatically. It will be as if invisible hands are helping you lay the foundation for a new adventure. You may feel swept away into a totally new existence. And you may feel a bit scared as everything you have learned up until now, no longer seems to serve you.

Different rules apply on this journey. There seem to be different laws of time and space. Your spontaneous impulses will often fly in the face of all rules and guidelines the world agrees on. Your spontaneous impulses will liberate you to another plane of power and freedom."

- GARRET LOPORTO, THE DAVINCI METHOD

I have always lived as if every day was my last, and the message I was getting after reading this piece, and the gut feeling that followed, was enough to send me on this mad journey that I'm so close to completing!

Everyone knows about gut instincts, and people with ADD ADHD will generally go with gut instincts, more so than 'normals'. One day you will read or see or even hear something that just makes all your thoughts click into place - the day you go into business is a good example. Sometimes you just need the extra confidence to proceed with all your dreams. Believe it or not people with this condition can be very shy and not so confident deep down, but once they start to believe in themselves, there's no stopping them.

The secret is to unlock the "fire in the belly" and follow your heart a little more, let yourself go a bit and reach for the stars - your dreams will only come true if you make them come true, and the only way that it is likely to happen is by you making it happen. 'You will never know until you try' is a great phrase, and so true in this life, and when you take into account also that 'you only live once' and 'life is too short', then this is definitely a gamble you should have a punt on!

If you can't believe in yourself then there will never be any hope, I'm a firm believer that anything is possible if you put your mind to it, and so far I'm realising that you only get back what you put in, which applies to life as a whole as well by the way!

Seize the opportunity, and if the opportunity isn't there, then go and make your own! At the end of the day what have you really got to lose? You will know when the time is right and you will feel "the fire in the belly" and when you do, go for it! Don't even think about it, just do it!

13. Summing up, and Good Advice

If you are little confused about things after reading the book, then hopefully this section will fill in some of the gaps.

General summing up, good phrases to remember, and the odd example thrown in for good measure.

This book will cause a little bit of controversy - well, how could anyone with ADHD write a book and it be anything other? But it is full of new facts and information about this condition, and of course many may say that some or all of these are total rubbish, while some others hopefully will find it really very helpful indeed!

Useful sayings to remember:

Change the way you look at things, and the way things look will change!

Less haste, more speed!

It doesn't matter how many knockdowns you get, what matters is how high you bounce back.

In for a penny, in for a pound.

You only get back what you put in!

Live every day as if it were your last!

For every action, there's a reaction.

Treat others like you would expect them to treat you.

Don't eat yellow snow.

God loves a trier.

One for the road is often one too many.

To the Many People Who Influenced This Book, I Offer Thanks

There is only one name deserving to top this list, and that belongs to my gorgeous wife, Marju Bradshaw: I thank you for helping me through each day, and for putting up with my many faults and foibles! Without you this book, the film and the soundtrack couldn't have happened!

Thanks too to my wonderful sons Maxx and Travis, for giving me the inspiration to better myself, and to give me the goal of making their lives as good as I possibly can.

I would like also to thank one of my DJ friends, Yannis Gorak. Yannis has inspired me with his knowledge of this condition, and his approach to how he deals with his ADHD has helped make my own life a lot better! I appreciate all of his input into this book and this has been a team effort of sorts (even though I've done so much more than you lot - lol!)

A very big thank you also to my director Hambi Haralanbous, who while he has had no direct input into the book, has insights into ways to get my head around the condition which have proven astonishing! These have changed the way I've written the book, for the better I might add.

Garret Lo Porto the author of The Davinci Method the book that changed my life for the better.

Thanks to my Mum and Dad for struggling through life with the devil for a son, you both deserve a medal and I'm forever grateful to you both!

Thanks to my good mate Paul Taylor, all those Tapman's walks over two summers opened my eyes to a different side to this condition and your input and thoughts have also proved hugely influential. A big thank you for that!

Thanks to my artist Kit Nelson, who four years ago gave me a book to read on ADHD and said he thought I might have the condition. That book changed my life for the better, without doubt!

Thanks to all my close friends who never stopped believing in me, even when many others did! I won't forget that, ever!

Thanks also to the wonderful people of Ibiza for giving me a second home and the most amazing memories over the years! And finally thank you to the Isle of Man for giving me the most incredible childhood!

Thanks to Yanni's dad Patrick Jozef Gorak for correcting my appalling spelling.

Thanks to chrisbevanphotography.co.uk